FABULOUS, FANTASTIC FELLINI!

"FILM GENIUS FELLINI IS AT IT AGAIN! The most inventive and controversial film director in the world, the man who made 'La Strada,' 'La Dolce Vita,' and '8½,' has just finished what devotees are calling his ninth and a half movie!"—LIFE

"A VISUAL KNOCKOUT! AN EYE-FILLING SPECTACLE OF THE PSYCHE...Peopled by marvelously bizarre characters, scenes wilder than 'La Dolce Vita,' stunning women in fantastic costumes, and weird, audacious situations. AN EYE-POPPING TWO-AND-ONE-HALF HOURS OF RAZZLE-DAZZLE FELLINI!"

—WILLIAM WOLF, Cue Magazine

"TRULY A CINEMATOGRAPHIC MIRACLE! AN EXCITING EXPERIENCE ON THE SCREEN!"

—BOSLEY CROWTHER, New York Times

Gramley Library
Salem College
Winston-Salem, NC 27108

[CONTINUED]

"A MASTERWORK WHOSE BEAUTY BE-LITTLES ADJECTIVES! Certainly one of the most beautiful and stimulating films ever made!"

—JUDITH CRIST, New York Herald Tribune

'BEAUTIFUL! HALLUCINATORY! EXTRAOR-DINARY PICTORIAL BEAUTY! I AM FAIRLY SURE THAT YOU WILL NEVER HAVE LOOKED UPON A MORE RAVISHING PICTURE!"

—BRENDAN GILL, The New Yorker

AND HERE IT IS—the complete story of "Juliet of the Spirits"! Prefaced by the longest interview Fellini has ever granted, here is the original screenplay *and* the transcript of the film as it was finally made by the most dazzling film genius of our time!

Illustrated with 32 pages of photographs.

FEDERICO FELLINI'S

JULIET
OF
THE
SPIRITS

edited by Tullio Kezich
translated from the Italian by
Howard Greenfeld

Transcription of final screen play by John Cohen

Translation by Cecilia Perrault

WITHDRAWN

BALLANTINE BOOKS　　●　　NEW YORK

Gramley Library
Salem College
Winston-Salem, NC 2710⌀

All rights reserved
Translation copyright © 1965 by Grossman Publishers, Inc.
Translated from *Giulietta degli Spiriti* by Federico Fellini.
Originally published by Casa Ed. L. Cappelli, Bologna, Italy, 1965.
From the film collection *Dal soggetto al film*
edited by Renzo Renzi.
Back cover photo: Franco Pinna from Rapho Guillumette
Transcription and Translation of
Final Screen Play Copyright © 1966 by
Ballantine Books, Inc.
First Printing: January, 1966
Library of Congress Catalog Card Number: 65-27273
Manufactured in the United States of America

BALLANTINE BOOKS, INC.
101 Fifth Avenue, New York, N. Y. 10003

Along with Federico Fellini, without whose coopera-tion this book would have been impossible, we would like to thank Clemente Fracassi, Luigi de Santis, and Ettore G. Mattia and the photographers Franco Pinna and G. B. Poletto.

TWENTY YEARS LATER

An introduction by Tullio Kezich

The character he has described on the screen, as no one else could have done. A black, wide-brimmed hat, a dark suit hanging loosely, the head by now shiny behind what was once a thick head of hair. He is the Director—no adjectives —the figure that best plays this role: king of a noisy, disordered court, despotic commander of an effervescent, fanatic crew. Every time he moves on the set, cameras snap, television cameras roll, tape recorders take down his every word. This is the tribute he pays to success. Everything urges him to act a part, to give a show, rather than to work. Work has become a kind of counterfeit remake of his film confession—another film within a film, a constant comedy, a Pirandello situation.

Wherever he shoots, there is an air of conspiracy, as if all have agreed to force him out of himself, to become someone else—the character they want to see, the artist who creates, the juggler who reveals his tricks, the clown who entertains. Lenses creak, pens fill notebooks; a hundred observers are ready to put down what he says, what he whispers, perhaps even what he thinks. It is as if a writer had to write, think, go over his work with people constantly reading over his shoulder. The work of the cinema is done in public, and Federico Fellini's public is the most varied. Around him while he works are people keeping appointments, friends coming to encourage him, enemies coming to envy him, gossips coming to spy on him. Comments are made on the events of the day; interesting meetings are held; friendships are made stronger or are broken. He says he hates this atmosphere of the waiting room or the hotel lobby, but he lives within it and can't do anything about it. It's his way of working, his way of existing. When Fellini says, "Camera," all that's missing is a playback of the little march from 8½ to complete the feeling of watching a circus act. And even the skeptics, those who think that watching the shooting of a film is the most boring thing in the world, fall into the trap. One day there are trained horses and elephants, the next day the grandfather's early airplane is found hanging from a crane way above the set, and the next there appear groups of mysterious beauties in topless dresses and hordes of fantastic barbarians, waiting their turn to come onto the scene.

Juliet of the Spirits proclaims itself the general activation, the illustrated catalogue of Fellini's universe. There is no fantasy, no memory, no color that Federico has hesitated to integrate into this joyful and tender total representation. *8½* penetrated the dominion of dreams and of individual fantasies; *Juliet* aims at a materialization of the magic world. He denies this only out of modesty, out of knowledge of his own limitations, out of humility. But the enjoyment, the pleasure of the unusual, takes us from one image to another in a kind of Mozartian counterpoint. Everthing could be as Juliet, or Giulietta, sees things; reality and imagination could exchange roles, and the series of fantastic illusions are about to vanish like a dream on the appearance of a golden morning. But what exists, concrete and tangible, behind the spectacle, what remains of so many images, apparitions, sounds, sensations, all as unforeseeable as human existence, is a moral conquest. The awareness of oneself, of one's own presence in the world, of one's right to exist. The comforting sense of necessity, of a superior harmony of opposites. The conviction that, beyond episodes and feelings, it is essential to reach—with the means that nature gives us—a balance of happiness.

The true alchemy of Fellini is his ability to touch a profound human note at the same time he mobilizes an undisciplined and indecipherable universe. It could be a lesson to those who claim to be upset and confused by modern life. What Fellini has learned in these last years, going beyond the rather mystical enchantment of his early efforts, is a kind of availability of consciousness. He has been open to every perceptible revelation, closed only to adulterations of the myth imposed by others. He is today like an older brother who has learned something about real wisdom.

The revelations are simple—preliminary steps, first letters of an alphabet—but to us they seem unassuming, solid points, small victories to celebrate together.

The words to describe Fellini in his thirties, from *The White Sheik* to *La Dolce Vita,* were picaresque, vagabond, troubled. Quantity, multiplicity, variety characterized his life and his work. In these last years, coming into his forties, the artist seems intent on considering quality. He is on the point of decisive discoveries, which he will grasp or touch according to his inspiration and good fortune. But in his search—what he calls work, cinema—he is totally committed, without reservations, within margins that are frighteningly small even as regards himself as an individual.

Consequently, Fellini equals *8½,* which equals *Juliet of the Spirits,* which equals the film he will make next, which he is already thinking about. In the enormous industry of this celebrated rogue there is not a grain of complacency, of laziness, of what is called living on one's income. The lucky gambler, who has spent half his life in front of the green table and has almost always won, continues to risk all on single numbers without spreading out the risk.

Federico's temperament is that of the explorer, the experimenter, the traveler without luggage. He goes ahead recklessly, sometimes vacillating and hesitating, but burning his bridges behind him. He denies himself the relief of imagining an honorable retreat. His would be a romantic position, all or nothing, if it were not tempered by an ironic skepticism and by a capacity for self-criticism even greater than he knows.

For this introduction to *Juliet,* the conversational form seems best suited to focus on certain subjects, to point out some features of this latest work. It is a conversation away from the chaos and the confusion, in Fellini's home on via Archimede, with Fellini usually stretched out on a sofa after a hard day's work while Giulietta watches television in the next room. The telephone is silent, and the discussion moves ahead freely, as happens between friends in the small hours of the morning. At other times we are barricaded in what

Gramley Library
Salem College
Winston-Salem, NC 27108

Fellini calls "the sanctuary of divine love," the little room with all the prizes, the walls covered with certificates, the room full of gold and silver cups and statuettes.

Federico is generous with himself, enough of an extrovert to allow a free dialogue. He is only afraid of seeming pedantic, presumptuous, or hypocritically modest: of speaking from a lofty position of an experience he doesn't yet feel is sufficient, of a success he rejects as qualified. To read this long interview—and interview is not really the right word—one must imagine Federico's calculated tones, his hesitations, his smiles, his sudden rearing back, his noble reservations. That is, to have him be present, in what we might call his disarming and complicated simplicity.

This was not a series of conversations between a critic and a director, between a journalist and a public figure. In such cases, most of the time, Federico takes the upper hand, writes the article by proxy, both to present himself and his work in the best possible way and to protect the film with which he is identified. It seemed useless to us to try to extract from one of the most interviewed members of the cinema world a series of unpublished confessions. We tried instead, observing the friendly rules of a talk between friends, to trace the lines of his poetics, the consistencies of his work. Fellini does not have real shop secrets; he allows anyone to poke his nose behind the scenes of his personal theater; but he rebels against any summary of data gathered in this way, at any attempt to build a methodology around him. He reserves the right to contradict himself, though he is one of the most consistent of artists; he does not want to be anchored to any limiting formula; this is the substance of his argument with neorealism—the pride of his position as an isolated man.

In reality, Rossellini's neorealism has probably had no more inspired follower than Fellini. Others have taken from that experience the journalistic, documentary, and historical aspects; they have added to the debt that the Italian cinema already owed to the French realists, the Soviet revolutionaries, and the American makers of Westerns. For Fellini, instead, the famous trip made for *Paisan*, his discovery of Italy, was the first stop of an inner itinerary, coming into contact with the submerged reality of our country: the faces, voices, dialects, ancestral myths, the purest hopes for the future. The world of Fellini has stepped over every literary or theatrical barrier, over every barrier of language or of class. His stories are not lessened by the lack of a spoken Italian; they take place naturally in a slanglike mosaic of present-day languages. Certain sterile theorizations of the negative hero and the positive hero have never prevented the director from expressing his own vision—even if only temporary, always in a state of elaboration and development—of our society from the postwar years until today. While the poetics of neorealism were becoming a kind of precept, few people had faith in the first experiments of a director who stood apart. And the first important opinions, destined to form the platform of his future work, came from foreign countries, because the majority of Italians were unable to place Fellini's experiences in a vast enough perspective.

Today the most probable relationships that Fellini is discovering (out of curiosity, out of ignorance, he insists) are with certain forms of avant-garde cinema between the two wars, especially the cinema linked to parallel disturbances. The most obvious difference is that in his most recent films, the figurative shock, the semantic surprise, are never expressed; they are fused with a commentary that is ever more obvious and linear. It is not so much a matter of narrative composition as it is of a natural arrangement of reflection. There are certain elements always present in the avant-garde but always extraneous to Fellini; he remains close to his calling as a storyteller, committed to offer us the fable and the moral of the fable.

The story of Federico Fellini is that of a faithful, determined, stubborn servant of his own calling. He does not deviate from this because of chatter, appearances, habits. He has been as out of date as today he is up to date, because he is not interested in adjusting his work to the current taste. That such a nature should find a place in the heart of the forest of the cinema, where so many stumble around in darkness and in the quicksand of daily compromise, is, at the very least, unusual.

There is an evident desire to know more about the artist.

the man—his experience, the goals he has set for his work, that "clear, useful art which will serve tomorrow" of which Marcello spoke in Steiner's salon (in *La Dolce Vita*). The appearance of *Juliet of the Spirits* is important. After *8½*, one could have presumed that Fellini had reached the end of his repertory, that his whole world was unwound in the beautiful confusion around the first-person hero. Instead, out of that explosion of egocentricity, a more objective, unbridled artist was born, faithful to autobiographical works but in a different and allusive form. Our discussion was written down, in notes which do not pretend to any organization, during December 1964 and January 1965, toward the end of the filming of *Juliet*. His greatest work behind him, able to look at his film in a broad context, it is natural enough for the author to begin to draw some conclusions. This is the memorandum of the "novel of a novel" that Fellini will never write. And it is also an attempt to bring together materials for a critical reflection on an artistic phenomenon who spontaneously takes his place at the intersection of a hundred roads and is as precious as the most rarefied experience, as shamelessly listenable as a successful advertising slogan.

TULLIO KEZICH

PART ONE

THE LONG INTERVIEW

PROSPERO: *Be collected;*
No more amazement. Tell your piteous heart
There's no harm done.

                    —THE TEMPEST, Act 1, Scene 2

THE LONG INTERVIEW

Tullio Kezich & Federico Fellini

THE GREAT WALL OF CHINA

Twenty years have passed since Open City, *your real beginning in the cinema, your first important screenplay. If you think back to this period, what do you feel?*

I have to confess something that will cut this short. I remember very little. It seems to me that I have a poor memory; it's hard for me to remember the things I invent. Maybe I still can concentrate on my work. When I am shooting a film, it seems to me I'm attentive enough and remember almost everything—at least the essential things. By now, my work coincides with my own life; I completely identify with whatever I'm doing. Even though, thinking it over carefully, this was true only up to two years ago. It's still true, but a little less so. I'm beginning to be able to think of myself apart from my work, more at peace, like someone who makes a film every once in a while. Nonetheless, it's difficult for me to have a complete awareness of this.

You mean that you feel a certain repugnance at the thought of telling about all the events of your life and of your career?

Repugnance is not the right word. Let's say biological incapacity.

There must have been, in your professional career, some element that establishes a kind of before and after—a fact, an important encounter.

17

Rossellini, but as a kind of underground passage that helped me cross the street. I don't think he profoundly influenced me in the usual sense of the word. In relation to myself, I recognize in him a kind of paternity, like that of Adam, a kind of progenitor from whom we are all descended. It's not easy to point out exactly what I inherited from him. Roberto encouraged me to come out of a foggy, indecisive period, into the arena of the cinema. It was an important meeting, and the films I made with him were important. But it was a matter of destiny, without any clarity or will on my part. I was ready for any undertaking, and he was there.

Didn't you begin in the movies with the idea of becoming a director?

No. I thought I wasn't cut out for that. I lacked any taste for tyrannical oppression; I lacked consistency, the ability to stick to details, the ability to wear myself out, and many other things. But above all I lacked authority. All these qualities were not in my temperament. As a child, I was very timid, solitary, vulnerable to the point of fainting. And I've remained very shy, even though people don't think so. With all these characteristics, how could I get along with the high boots, the megaphones, the shouting—the traditional arms of the cinema? The director of a film is always in command of Christopher Columbus' crew, a crew that wants to turn back. All around are the faces of electricians with their silent question: "What, are we going to work late again tonight?" If you didn't have a little authority, they'd very affectionately throw you out of the theater.

When did you feel that you were able to direct?

Late, very late, when I was already in so deep that I couldn't pull out. I was already writing the screenplays, so I would go on the set to change situations or scenes. I was amazed that the director could have detached relationships with the actresses. It was hard for me to write dialogue in the midst of that confusion; I felt very ill at ease working collectively, everyone doing something together and talking loudly. However, as you know, it's ended up that I can now work well only in the midst of confusion, just as when I was a journalist I wrote articles at the last minute in the chaos of the city room.

I felt a little more at ease doing films that were shot outdoors, in the open. Rossellini really started this. The experience with Roberto, the trip we took for *Paisan*, represented the discovery of Italy for me. Until that time, I hadn't seen very much—Rimini, Florence, Rome, some small towns in the south I had seen while traveling with the variety shows, little towns and villages enclosed in a medieval night, like those we knew as children, but with different dialects. I liked the way Roberto made his films—a pleasant journey, a trip to the country with friends. When, later on, I had doubts and fears about becoming the director of my first film, it was to these early, happy memories that I returned to gather courage.

What was your first film—Variety Lights, *which you made with Alberto Lattuada, or* The White Sheik?

Both, in different ways. *Variety Lights* had been my idea, and I felt it was a film of mine. It contained memories, some true and some invented—a certain feeling for the provinces that I knew very well. But Lattuada was there to back me up, with his ability to make decisions, with his experience, with his little whistle. He was the director: He said, "Roll, action, stop, everyone out, silence." I was at his side, in a rather happy position of irresponsibility. *The White Sheik* was a strange situation. Antonioni was supposed to direct it, but he didn't like the screenplay that Pinelli and I had done. Finally, Rovere told me that I should direct it. I didn't decide to become a director; it was the somewhat imprudent faith of Luigi Rovere that pushed me into it. He decided that I had to do the picture, and he placed at my side a production director who made me tremble. Enzo Provenzale had just collaborated with Germi, a real director, very capable, well prepared technically, precise, tough. Through an excess of affection, he would have wanted me to become another Germi at once. And I, in the meantime, couldn't sleep at night. Well, in the beginning you asked me when I felt I could become a director; now it seems to me I remember the precise moment: the first day of work on *The White Sheik*.

It's a true story, but every time I tell it people look at me as if I'm telling some invented anecdote. However, it did happen just like this. One morning I found myself on a small boat, which, having left the pier at Fiumicino, was on its way to meet a motor fishing boat on the high seas that was carrying the cast and crew of *The White Sheik*. They were waiting for me to start shooting; they were waiting for the director. I had said good-bye to Giulietta, almost at dawn, with the same beating of the heart and fear the schoolboy has when he goes to take exams. I even went to church, attempting a prayer. I took my car, and on the road to Ostia one of my tires blew out. The troupe, as I told you, had already embarked. And down there, in the middle of the sea, I saw my destiny. I was to shoot a very complicated scene between Sordi and Brunella Bovo. As I approached the fishing boat, I saw the faces of the workmen, the lights already on. I kept repeating to myself: "What will I do now?" I didn't remember the film any more, I didn't remember anything. All I wanted to do was escape. But as soon as I set foot on that fishing boat, I was giving orders, commanding this one and that one, looking inside the camera—without knowing anything, without knowing what I wanted. In the few moments between the pier and the fishing boat, I had become a demanding, detail-conscious, capricious director with all the defects and all the good qualities that I had always envied in real directors.

What was, then, the decisive push that brought you to the cinema?

I would say it was a rather mysterious calling. I must repeat that my temperament was leading me elsewhere. Even today, when my picture is finished, I am surprised. How the devil have I been so active, how have I been able to get so many people moving, make choices a thousand times a day, say no to this and yes to that?

Is it true that you never go to the movies? Many people say that you pretend this lack of interest in order to avoid seeing the films of others or to avoid admitting having seen them. So did you begin not going to the movies when you became a director, or didn't you go even before, when you were a child, a young man?

I spoke of a calling for the cinema, but I can't even say that as a child I went often. Most of the time I didn't have the money, they didn't give it to me. Then, the movie house I used to go to—the Fulgor at Rimini! In the cheap seats, those under the screen, they really used to give it to the shy boys like myself. There was an uproar such as I've never heard since. My first memory of a film goes back to *Maciste all' inferno*, I think. I was in my father's arms, the house was packed, it was hot and they kept spraying an antiseptic that grated the throat and dazed me. In that slightly opiate atmosphere I remember the yellowish images on the screen of all kinds of people in Hell. Then I remember shots of priests in a large room with wooden benches, black-and-white shots of churches, Assisi, Orvieto. But I remember, above all, the posters. They really enchanted me. I remember one evening, with a friend, cutting out with a razor, pictures of Ellen Meis, an actress I really thought beautiful. She was in a film of Maurizio d'Ancora's, *Venere*, I think.

Were you interested in the story of the film or the way it was told?

Only the story. Even later I paid no attention to close-ups, techniques, etc. I don't know the classics of the cinema. I'm ashamed to admit it, but I've never seen any Murnau, Dreyer, or Eisenstein. When I came to Rome, I went to the movies more often—once a week or once every two weeks. When I didn't know where else to go, or when there was a variety show with the picture. I was always thrilled by the shows that preceded a movie, as by a circus. For me a movie house is a room bubbling with noises and odors; chestnuts, the urine of children; that feeling of the end of the world, of disaster. The confusion that comes before the stage show—the musicians arriving in the pit, the voice of the comedian, the sounds of the girls behind the curtains. Then the people who go out the fire exit in the winter, into an alley, made children again by the cold; someone hums a tune from the picture, people laugh . . .

But beyond these impressions of the atmosphere of the movie house, haven't there been any movies that have greatly impressed you, any that you especially liked?

Of course. I was moved to tears by *City Lights*. And John Ford's *The Informer* is unforgettable; the music still haunts me. I liked *The Thin Man* with William Powell, the musicals, the Fred Astaire pictures, the Marx brothers. After the war I saw *Sergeant York* and was somewhat disappointed. Then Sonia Henie in a musical that had a beautiful boogie-woogie, but that smacked a little of the prehistoric. I thought right away that there was nothing to be hoped for from that area any more. I liked *Monsieur Verdoux;* I think it's Chaplin's best picture, perhaps the most beautiful film I've ever seen. In a moment of relaxation, of false serenity, he made a desperate film, a film of almost prophetic intuition. I don't fundamentally agree with his graveyard vision, but I think this is his limit as a man and not as an artist.

Is it true that in recent years you haven't gone to the movies at all, or have you seen some films that you have liked?

I'm not taking into consideration private screenings, given for professional reasons, of films on which I've worked or films of friends or films I've been forced to see. Sometimes someone goes around saying that I saw his film and that I'm very enthusiastic about it. It may not be true, but it could be, because I basically like everything I see on the screen. Even in an atmosphere that is certainly different from the one I knew as a child and as an adolescent, in a rather ascetic atmosphere, there's always an enchantment, which I don't give in to easily, but which always does get to me. If you want to get away from generalizations, I'll name some films that I have seen and liked. I would say that I liked *Wild Strawberries* very much—more than I would if I thought it over or if I saw it again. I'm not a good critic and I'm a very poor witness; I distort everything and am very prone to take sides. I don't like arguments, and discussions bore me. I feel that *Wild Strawberries* and also *The Magician* are very close to my own temperament. I've never met Bergman, but I feel close to him through his films. He is a conjurer—half witch and half showman. I also like his tricks, the spectacle made from nothing. They tell me he is no longer fashionable in certain intellectual circles, but it doesn't matter to me. He is really a great film maker. Another of his standing is Akira Kurosawa. Watching *Roshomon* or *Seven Samurai,* I became a boy again; I feel an unqualified admiration. And then, recently, I liked *The Birds* very much; I have fought with everyone about it. It's a perfect movie—precise as a miniature. For the whole first half, the tranquillity and well-being of that couple—a brilliant contrivance. I don't measure adjectives when I find something I like, nor does my enthusiasm cool off with critical considerations. For me criticism is a kind of masochism. Why reevaluate something that has moved you, water it down, control it, kill it?

Let's return to your career as a film maker. If you had to pass through these twenty years again, is there anything that you would change?

You're asking the kind of question that presupposes my acceptance of a certain journalistic game. However, even going along with the game, I don't think I would change anything. Maybe I would have liked to have started earlier, that is, to have already been a director in 1920, to be twenty years old then, to be a part of the pioneering period. When I made my first film, the cinema was already an archaeological fact, with a history and an aesthetic. There had already been a process of intellectualization; there were comparisons, curbs. In the beginning, however, there weren't these complications. Everything was more modest, new, free. I often say that I began making films as if the cinema did not exist, but that's being a little too detached. The rhetoric of others, the poetics, a half century of images—these have thrown many shadows, exerted influences on my work, and perhaps they have prevented a complete spontaneity.

As a person, have you changed in any way—your mentality, your habits? Do you feel different?

I would say so. My attitudes toward both people and things are the same. It's a matter of character, determined by educational conditioning. I'm still a little ill at ease because I have a complex about being a little schoolboy—intimidated but somewhat naughty; I'm not mentally free of this.

You remember the producer we went to see together today. I'm ready to tear that kind of man to pieces when it comes to work. However, that man, apart from work, makes me uneasy, makes me feel profoundly inferior. In front of him I again become a boy, placed under paternal authority, whether it be threatening or benevolent.

As you certainly know, I'm not at all self-possessed. I'm barely sociable at all. Groups frighten me. I never go to parties, to lectures, to debates. They always seem things that don't concern me, things for grownups. It's not a matter of pride, it's not a false sense of superiority. It's not even always a feeling of inferiority. It's detachment.

Are there any exceptions to this noninvolvement with public events or issues?

Yes. If there is a collective protest against something that might violate or tend to suppress any profoundly individual freedom, I get angry and can even go to meetings, if not to the barricades. In other, milder situations, I stand apart, knowing very well that I would not be useful.

What about the public image of Fellini do you like, and what bothers you?

Every time I feel that people have confidence in me, I am satisfied. It flatters me even when I feel it shows up my shortcomings. What I hate, on the other hand, is the official aspect, the decorative one—the ceremonies, prizes, going up to the stage, taking the statuette, thanking, speaking. I've had to get used to it, sullenly, but it's always like swallowing a pill.

But don't you think that receiving no recognition at all would be worse?

I know what you mean, but it's hard for me to explain myself without seeming hypocritical. If I were to say to you that prizes mean nothing to me and never have, you probably wouldn't believe me. So I will limit myself to saying that I really have no competitive spirit. Contests, classifications established by juries, races to see who arrives first—I'm always out of these. I'm not interested in sports; I've never even been to a soccer game. Of course, prizes are pleasing. I'd be a liar if I said the opposite. But I can also add that when I don't get them I don't suffer a bit.

It was the same way with women when I was a boy. I never competed with anyone. Fights, whether based on strength or cleverness, have never appealed to me; I don't know if the repugnance is biological or spiritual. To be completely honest, I will add that my shyness may be concealed by an extremely pugnacious, crafty, efficient attitude. When I can really force myself to want something, I can become more active, lucid, and inventive than others who identify themselves with their desires. Only this fact justifies the myth of my craftiness.

You said, speaking of the films that you saw and liked, that you're incapable of critical reflection. Is this true even with your own work?

I am the last one to have any rational, critical idea about

what I do. For this reason I admire Pasolini, who can go
from creative outbursts to helpful, positive critical reflections. For me, however, reflection always results in a para-
lyzing doubt and anxiety. It might be because I don't have
the right tools, the cultural preparation; if I reason in
critical terms, I enter into a swamp without an exit. Look:
the film has fifteen more days to go, and I don't know how
it's going to end. I really don't know—that is, I know what
I want to express, but I'm unable to see any images.

Last night I dreamed of Giulietta in the middle of an
empty setting, with the camera on a dolly shooting around
her; the dolly was loaded with people making a great noise,
buffoons. I tried to give orders, instructions, but the bawling
of the people on the dolly covered up my voice, until they
all collapsed to the ground. Maybe the dream means that I
am shooting around the subject and that there is the risk of
a general collapse. I sensed the atmosphere of a shipwreck,
and I woke up terrified.

*These crises of yours at the end of a film are habitual.
For many years I've seen you worried about the end of a
film. For* La Dolce Vita, *you were undecided between two
endings and you shot both of them; the same thing happened with 8½.*

That's not true. I thought of two, three, a hundred endings for *La Dolce Vita,* but I only shot one. For *8½,* on the
other hand, I shot a different ending. Marcello and his
wife in the dining car, surrounded by all the characters in
the film. As an ending it was perhaps more beautiful than
the other, but the one I chose was more honest, more in
keeping with the tone of the film. In any case, I admit that
even this time it's the same story. This both comforts and
alarms me. It comforts me because the other times I pulled
out of it and so should pull out of it this time. It alarms
me because this indecision of mine is not part of my decep-
tions, it's not a slightly superstitious mechanism that I put
into motion to stimulate creativity. It is a real, concrete
abyss that I reach every time, with the risk of breaking my
neck. The risk, that is, of working on the irrational bases of

sensitivity and inspiration—if I may use a slightly irritating term. There is nothing concrete, nothing that can be calculated, nothing foreseeable.

I was about to say that with *Juliet of the Spirits* I might have lost the use of my right eye, that of reality. That reminds me of another dream, one I had a week before starting the film. Someone suddenly took out my right eye with a spoon. I didn't feel pain; I was just surprised. What did that dream mean? I can't really say. Maybe it meant that for this picture I didn't need the concrete, earthly right eye but only the left—the one of fantasy. But it could also have been a dream admonishing me: You will end badly, you no longer have a right eye, you see things too one-sidedly.

Do you attach much importance to dreams?

Yes, but we should attach even greater importance to them. Trying to interpret them is, if nothing else, a fascinating psychological game. Someone has said that they are fables we tell ourselves, myths that help us understand. Naturally we shouldn't ask the immediate and continual help of dreams to change our daily behavior. And we shouldn't abandon ourselves completely to the nocturnal spectacle. The habitual dreamer takes the risk of spending the whole day doing nothing between the evanescent and the crumbling. One could be so immersed in waiting for the night in order to dream that the images are no longer of any use.

What do you think of other people, in general? Your relations with friends, acquaintances, the hundreds of people you meet? Do they enrich you, or do you prefer to be alone?

I like other people when they are in harmony, above all the people I work with and my friends. It's not altruism; I like them to be in harmony because then they leave me in peace. I always fear the worst from discord and from fights. I feel very well when I'm alone; I never feel the weight of solitude. But I also feel fine with others. I'm ill at ease only when I'm in those gatherings we spoke of before, get-to-gethers without any meaning or purpose, with people who chatter, who exchange news and smiles. To meet people I hardly know, to go to crowded restaurants to talk—these are real tortures for me. You asked me before if I have changed my habits. The truth is that I have none; I do everything except these things. And also, I don't feel well when I travel.

Not feeling well when you travel implies that you are tied to habits and customs. It seems to me that you are contradicting yourself.

Well? However, in this case the contradiction is only on the surface. Travel bothers me not because it breaks certain daily rhythms. And it's necessary to make a distinction: when I travel around Italy, everything is fine. The sights of the cities are accented, the dialects are different but still comprehensible, there is a common root that is sufficiently elastic to take in almost all the stimuli. It's traveling in foreign countries that always disturbs me, countries that are indecipherable, that I'm unable to penetrate.

You know that Freud calls the unconscious the "internal foreign country," that is, the personal foreign country of each of us?

I think this identification of the unconscious with a foreign country is very valid. The most disturbing dream or daytime fantasy, at home, or anyway in the great maternal womb of Rome, can leave me with a perspiring forehead or a heavily beating heart, but they are always stimulating. Here I feel I can enjoy even fear, but far away, in the middle of an unknown world, fear can become worrisome.

You speak a great deal about anxiety and fear. Is there something that frightens you today, or has maturity changed this aspect of your personality?

There has been a maturing, and it was time that there was.

I think I can take care of myself better. But I don't want to sound too happy with myself. All the more so because this apparent maturity can be suddenly contradicted. In fact, perhaps the feeling of being able to control emotional states comes not from a real maturity, but simply from an aging, that is, a thickening of a remote ancestral opacity.

This feeling of having control is an unsteady one. It is difficult to be at peace, and when we are, we are rarely aware of it. All in all, I'm afraid I still have little irritations that I shouldn't have, treacherous fears. I am bothered by a kind of nostalgia for a more complete morality—this discomforts me, makes me gloomy. Perhaps it is true that one can't change completely, that the character formed in infancy determines the life of the mature man. Some call it destiny; others attribute it to emotional factors in the newborn. As far as I'm concerned, I think this conditioning comes from education, from the arbitrary or fanatical application of moral standards imposed in the sacred environment of the family, at an age when it is neither permitted nor possible to choose. We spend the second half of our lives wiping out the taboos, repairing the damage that education has caused in the first half. I'm speaking of men of my generation—I think this holds true for many.

It seems to me that this theme has dominated your recent films. La Dolce Vita approached it, in an emotional manner, in the episode of the meeting between Marcello and his father. 8½, however, is a far clearer and more concise criticism of a kind of counterreformed education. And your Juliet is restrained as a human being within a debasing educational scheme; your film might be the story of her progressive liberation.

This is a fundamental theme for me, and I would like to go into it even more explicitly in the film I make after Juliet.

Does any one of your films represent you more completely than the others—a key film or, as we used to say, a film to preserve?

La Strada and *8½*. *La Strada* is really the complete catalogue of my entire mythical world, a dangerous representation of my identity, undertaken without precautions. Do you
like the definition? *8½* is meant to be an attempt to reach an
agreement with life.

*What are the terms of this? Do you feel that 8½ points
out one of the ways of being a man, of existing in the
world in relative peace with oneself and with others?*

I repeat that *8½* is an attempt and not a completed result.
I think for now it might indicate a solution: to make friends
with yourself completely, without hesitations, without false
modesty, without fears and without hopes.

Your journey from Zampanò of La Strada *to the director of* 8½ *is nonetheless a process of rationalization of the
self in a critical and self-educational sense. It seems to me
that, rather than scorning each rationalization, you con-
solidate your artistic and personal conquests in this hated
direction. Even though you always move on the level of the
individual dimension, the international success of your last
film contradicts you; and it should make you realize that
your individual solution might be valid—is valid—for
others. It seems to me that you have built a kind of Great
Wall of China within yourself, to defend you from the
monsters of your "personal foreign country." Yet it is really
from the unconscious, the fabulous, beyond that wall that
you receive the material for your stories. You have learned
to distribute these contributions sparingly so that they don't
overcome you and suffocate you. The dialectic between the
ancestral myth and a new morality, in a dimension that is
preferably ironic, is the key to all your work, and in these
last years it comes to the surface with extreme clarity.*

I hope you're right and that the wall is solid.

*You once spoke of the need to create a kind of connec-
tive tissue between one film and the next, an occupation*

for your idle periods. When you said this, did you have any
precise projects or ambitions?

When I was speaking of a connective tissue between one film and the next, I was either insincere or fooling myself. I've never had these idle periods in my life. I've never been on vacation; I am constitutionally incapable of thinking of periods of calm and immobility.

Would you like proof? A while ago, at the end of *8½*, I went through an experiment with LSD. A scientist friend of mine asked me to take part in the experiment, and I told him I'd like to try. Experiments with really sick people didn't seem to satisfy my friend or his colleagues; they liked the idea of having an artist in their hands, and I couldn't get out of it.

I was already compromised, and I didn't want to look like a coward. So, my heart beating fast, I went to the home of a chemist, not far from here, one Sunday afternoon after having fasted all day. There was my friend, with two nurses, a cardiologist, a battery of stenographers and microphones. They gave me an electrocardiograph—all was well. And then they gave me something diluted in water. The effect generally lasts between seven and eight hours, but with me it lasted even longer.

I can't say very much about what happened to me; I don't remember it very well. I know that in order to stop the effect they had to give me an intravenous tranquilizer. At ten at night they brought me home, and I spent a good enough night under medical surveillance. The next morning I awakened as if nothing, or almost nothing, had happened. I didn't want to hear the recordings of what I had said; shame had overcome curiosity. But they tell me that I spoke for seven or eight hours and that I paced up and down the room without stopping for a moment. This activity, or the thing that put the motor centers in motion, was interpreted by the experimenters as a flight, the impossibility of standing still. It could mean many things, but principally that my natural condition is to be in motion, on the move. As a matter of fact, I feel very well in a car, with the images rushing by outside the window. I repeat that I can't imagine myself having a quiet vacation.

Among your many restless habits, I have noticed your way of tearing up your mail after having quickly gone through it.

Yes. I can't keep anything in my pocket, I tear up everything; if Giulietta weren't there to stop me, I would do even worse. This is evidently an eccentric attempt to free myself from useless things, based on the slightly absurd hope of making a clean slate in order to start again from the beginning.

From what you say, as well as from your films, it seems obvious that you have a strong interest in psychoanalysis.

It is the interest of a dilettante, of a meddler greedy to gather facts. I know that psychoanalysis can be of great help to the sick. There are forms of neurosis that so greatly alter the psyche that they don't even leave a precise memory when they are over. As if one had been a fish at one time and wanted to tell about his experiences in the language of man. It is in these cases, when the fever is high and the condition is serious, that psychoanalysis can help. But it does not, I believe, always furnish the means to prevent a new attack. There is the danger of making it a collective cure-all, which explains everything and risks overlooking the individual.

So, what way out remains to a man who is going through a crisis?

I believe that life can always pull him out. There is always something in reserve. Life changes you; it can grind down within each one of us the heart-rending nostalgia for an ineffable morality and well-being, the regret for lost innocence. One can't live and work with an unsatisfied yearning for the conscience of an angel.

So you agree with what Wittgenstein writes—that the greatness of man is proportional to the amount of strength that his work costs him?

It's a very true and correct observation. Dignity, the only true dignity, is just this, to rediscover oneself in hard work.

HOW TO TELL A STORY

When did you begin to tell stories to yourself? Has there always been a relationship in your imagination between narrative invention and graphic representation? That is, between story and picture?

When I was a child, I used to build puppet shows by myself. First I would do a drawing on cardboard, then I would cut it out and put the heads together with clay or with paste-soaked wads. A friend of the family who was a sculptor used to come to my father's store; he saw what I was doing and he taught me to use a liquid glue. I would also make the colors myself, crushing tiles and reducing them to dust. I began to hang around artisans who were working in leather, and some carpenters who would give me soft wood. When I think about it, it seems to me that my imagination was always connected with craftsmanship.

I never cared about games except those dealing with puppet shows, colors, and construction: drawings that you cut out and paste together in perspective. For the rest, nothing; I never kicked a ball. I used to love to lock myself in the bathroom for hours on end, putting powder on my face and making up in the most incredible ways—egg whites on my head so my hair would stay down like a man's, whiskers drawn on with burned cork, and so on.

If in all this certain indications of my future can be seen, it might be that the elements were there. I've always felt very strongly, even as a spectator, the call of the theater. I will spare you the stories of my escape with the circus, which has already been told in many ways.

At school, much later on, I started a kind of illustrated

cartoon, with caricatures, little drawings and stories. If this is what you mean by a relationship between the graphic and the narrative, yes; it seems to me this has been the case, at least as a tendency.

Before going into the movies, did you ever think of painting or writing?

Until I went to school, I never asked myself the question; I could never project myself into the future. I thought of a profession as something that one couldn't avoid, like Sunday Mass. I never said: "When I grow up, I will . . ." It didn't seem to me that I would grow up—and basically I wasn't even wrong.

Maybe the only profession I would have accepted was that of an actor. Then I found myself writing a huge number of things. For years I wrote a radio program for sick people that was on every afternoon—songs, little stories, little sketches. I also wrote articles for newspapers, which also published my drawings. But I never took myself seriously as a graphic artist.

I have often seen you with watercolors while you were working on your films, even your black-and-white ones. I remember, for example, that I first saw one of your ideas for the Baths in 8½ in a drawing in which rose-colored transparencies hung above the trees like a kind of fog. Is this a method that goes back to your earliest films, or did you start doing this later?

I've always done that, from my first film on. Ever since I wrote sketches for variety shows, I've liked to do designs of the costumes. Any ideas I have immediately become concrete in sketches or drawings. Sometimes the very ideas are born when I'm drawing. Gelsomina, for example, came out of a drawing.

Later on, this habit became a necessity; I don't have to talk so much with my assistants; it's easier to show them what I want through my scribblings. Watercolors are also a way of concentrating on the problems of a film at a certain point in its preparation.

Why do you think you decided to use color—first for the episode in Boccaccio '70 *and now for* Juliet? *Was there an external factor, such as an offer from the producer, the possibility of doing it, or was it your own choice, an aesthetic one?*

The two cases are different. For the episode in *Boccaccio '70*, the choice wasn't mine. It was an "episodic film" and the producers decided it was to be in color. I didn't object at all. The playful air of the whole undertaking and the brief form of the episode seemed just right for an experiment with color without too great a commitment on my part. I didn't think about the problem very seriously; I didn't go into it deeply. In *Juliet*, on the other hand, color is an essential part of the film. I don't think I would have done it in black and white. It is a type of fantasy that is developed through colored illuminations. As you know, color is a part not only of the language but also of the idea and the feeling of the dream. Colors in a dream are concepts, not approximations or memories.

As in great painting?

Exactly: In a dream color is the idea, the concept, the feeling, just as it is in truly great painting. The question so many people ask, Do you dream in color or in black and white, is absurd. It's like asking if there are sounds in a song; everyone knows that sound is the way of expressing a song. The dreamer can see a red meadow, a green horse, a yellow sky—and they're not absurdities. They are images tempered with the feeling that inspires them.

Is it possible to translate all this into the cinema?

When I started to shoot the picture, I made a remark that has gone all around and is beginning to be a little disgusting: Cinema is movement; color is immobility; the fusion is impossible. It's a contradiction of terms, like breathing underwater. Forgetting the facile nature of the comment, it is just like that.

I must say that the use of color according to a rigorous plan is not possible. That is, you can't hope for a result that translates your ideas of color perfectly, without distortion or without at least modification, because there are unforeseeable elements in the lighting, the shooting itself, and the printing.

The painter gives to his painting a steady, unchangeable light. Color is an extremely personal factor, even on a physiological level. My green is not your green, nor that of a third person. Whoever paints can choose precisely the shade of color he wants. Someone may think that the same thing can be done in film, that it's enough to put the light on the element you want to bring out, and your green comes out. Let's say that it can be like this, although in fact there is a fluid interchange among the colors of a scene, because of which, during the projection, you realize that certain luminous areas are submerged in darkness and others have taken on unforeseeable reflections.

But let's say, for argument's sake, that the lighting is ideal. You look at the picture; you're satisfied and ready to shoot. At that point, obeying an instinct, you come closer or move farther back, you want another perspective, you move the camera even a little bit. Right away the intensity of the light changes, the color becomes brighter or duller; as soon as you have made the slightest move, the color values you have sought are no longer the same. The green is no longer your green.

The human eye sees things as the human eye, with all its weight of sentiment, ideas, the past. It is capable of making very rapid selections, of selecting the elements that strike it most forcefully. In our memory of things, a dominant color remains while the others disappear. If you were telling a friend about our meeting here and wanted to describe the colors of the room, you would probably remember only the gilding of that door, the light blue of this ashtray, the black of that painting. The camera doesn't work like that; it performs a purely mathematical function. It registers just what the light, which easily changes with each movement, offers to it, moment by moment.

The director of a color film is like a writer who, after having written "The room was green," finds it printed in the book as "The room was rose." Just like that—you shot a green room, and you go in the screening room and you see a rose room. Where was the rose?

I discovered this, the first time, with *Boccaccio '70.* I had thought of the character of Dr. Antonio as a small man, all in black, in the midst of the huge, very white buildings of the EUR. When I saw the projection, the marble was no longer white; it had become blue. The sky had reflected on the smooth parts of the buildings, and there was nothing to do about it.

Perhaps I should conclude that, since it's not possible to shoot films in color, only black and white should be used. However, despite all my disappointments, despite a feeling of angry impotence that poisoned months of my work, I feel that color adds a new dimension to a film like mine. Something that black and white could never have given it.

Do you think that color, which enriches the language, will become essential, just as sound has, or do you feel that black and white will remain an alternative even when there are no longer the problems you mention.

I don't think that color will completely replace black and white, but I do think—with all its unforeseeable and uncontrollable incongruities—it is a most important factor. I certainly prefer a black and white picture to a bad one in color. All the more so because in some cases the so-called natural color impoverishes the imagination. The more you mimic reality, the more you lose in the imitation. Black and white, in this sense, offers wider margins for the imagination. I know that after having seen a good black and white film, many spectators, when asked about its chromatic aspect, could say: "The colors were beautiful," because each one lends to the images the colors he has within himself.

So there are precise limitations that color imposes on the

*imagination of a director. But there is, on the other hand,
another side to this, isn't there?*

I am halfway through this experiment. I am fascinated by
it, but I haven't yet a thorough grasp of it. There is no
doubt that color produces an extraordinary result in many
scenes of this picture. I am thinking particularly of the
scene in Susy's house. The glass doors, the gauze, the shining
nylon, the sidewalks covered with glass that sends forth lights
—it's much more effective than it could ever have been in
black and white. No, color makes me angry every day; however, I already feel it's an integral part of my possibilities of
expression. And then, I don't want to defend black and
white, which is only a habit, at all costs.

While you were shooting Boccaccio '70, *you told me:
"There are only two colors you can use in the cinema—
black and white."*

That's a romantic, static, even reactionary position. I think
it's a tribute to the photography from which the cinema was
born. I've changed my mind.

*After this discussion of color, which represents one of the
newest aspects of* Juliet of the Spirits *in relation to your
other movies, I would like to try to trace the thread of one
of your enterprises in the cinema: the way in which you
come, each time, to tell a story to the public. It seems to
me that in your method (or lack of method, as you would
prefer to say) there are certain consistencies, rituals, that
are by now a part of your poetics. Let's not lose time by
speaking of how the ideas are born, because you can obviously tell me that they are born while you draw—as in the
case of Gelsomina—or while driving a car in Rome, or
while under the influence of a particular emotion or discovery. Let's go right to the first verifiable step—the screenplay. You've done screenplays for Rossellini, Lattuada and
Germi, so you've had specific experiences. Tell me what you
mean by screenplay, when it begins and when it ends.*

I suffered unbearably as a writer of screenplays. I must have been a very bad assistant for the director. I used to see the scene as a whole from the beginning; I scrupulously suggested all the details to the director. Even then I thought that the dialogue was of little importance. The tie that a character wore was more important than his conversation. Thus, while I was thinking of the knot and the color of that tie—things that weren't expected of me—Pinelli was writing. He has always written much more than I have, whenever we've worked together. His sound theatrical background enabled him to resolve a scene with good dialogue. There— Pinelli is a really good screenwriter.

Even now my attitude toward the screenplay has not changed. Sometimes during the dubbing of a film, I redo everything. Often, while I shoot, I prefer to have the actors recite numbers rather than sentences written months before, which I feel to be dated and out of place.

To answer your question right away—but I think we'll come back to this again—the screenplay begins with the idea and ends with the first copy, even the first showing of the film.

Then you don't accept the traditional phases of the work plan of a film?

The phases you talk about exist, and they do condition us. They are phases of production, contractual deadlines of convenience. They represent an inevitable model. But certainly, I would do without them if I could. A film is the work of an author in collaboration with everyone, really everyone—from the Eternal Father to the lowest bit player. I don't want to seem unappreciative of any of those who have worked with me or who are now working with me; on different levels they have all been most valuable to me. The screenwriters, above all: Pinelli and Flaiano, who have been by my side and have helped me for years in almost everything I've done. Along with them, Brunello Rondi—faithful, impassioned, full of ideas and enthusiasm. But how can you evaluate the imponderable—the right rain that suddenly begins to fall, a baby who really starts to cry, a visitor who arrives with a

hat that is immediately utilized to define a character who up
to that time was somewhat vague?

We need sorcerers in the cinema; the real work isn't making a choice of a character before or after, or deciding what
he has to say. That decision will come, and it will be the
right one, if you have been able to create a vital atmosphere
in which something might be born. Everything can come together to create this atmosphere, which first surrounds you
as an individual and then the set on which you work. When
I say everything, I mean even negative factors, the lack of
understanding, the difficulties, the delays.

Each time there is a time when I feel the screenplay isn't
sufficient, that it is useless to carry on further on a literary
level. Then I open my office. I call in people; I have hundreds of faces pass before me. It's a kind of ceremony to
create an atmosphere, one of many and certainly not the
most important. When I'm in my office, the door opens and
an old man comes in, a little girl, someone who wants to sell
a watch, a countess, a fat man. I see a hundred in order to
get two for the film; I compare clothing, dialects, whiskers,
tics, postures. Some poor man may be so happy because I
insist on having him photographed—and the only thing that
interests me is a picture of his eyeglasses. At a certain
point, I've had enough of the office and of the people passing in front of me, and then I begin the tests. This is the
definite phase of the ceremony. At this point, I know that in
a short time I have to begin the film.

From a certain moment the slackness, so useful and fer-
tile during other phases, becomes deadly. It is at this point
that difficulties and delays drive me mad, because I know that
it can't be put off any longer, that the race will be lost, that it
will become another film. And, once started, if the atmosphere
has reached the right point, there are no more difficulties. The
real effort is exerted in the preliminary phases. If all has gone
as it should, in spite of accidents and contradictions, if the
oxygen begins to circulate, nothing more is needed; actors,
places, dialogue. Everything can be changed; and everything
is, in fact, born, not respecting what you have prepared. At
this point, it is pointless to remain faithful to steps you have

made, to the choices made the day before yesterday, to something written five months before.

For a week or two I have to see if the film has been born and where it's going. It is the film that directs me; not I the film.

Maybe it's for this reason, to make it easier for you to know if the film has been born or not, that the precise dates when you start work on a film are so hard to establish. The same is true for the end of the film. The semiofficial date might be, as in the case of Juliet, *January 30—but there will certainly be additions and retakes. Thus the film will end secretly, just as it began. You would say it's not your fault; that when the film takes off, it goes wherever it wants to.*

For me, working on a film is a journey—I've said this so often that I hardly believe it any more. You don't take a journey in the abstract, but consider the exigencies that come up from hour to hour, your own mood, things that are impossible to predict. All that's required is an availability; you must allow yourself to be transported. Or, more precisely, you must put yourself in the hands of the thing that is to be born.

Let's speak about actors for a moment. Years ago, a friend of ours said to me: "When Federico gets together a cast, it's as if he were recruiting for the foreign legion." And you really always have had a weakness, I think, for bit players, unknown figures—even if this hasn't kept you from using important professional actors from time to time.

I don't see the problem that way. The importance of an actor, even his professional qualities, have never excited me, nor have they intimidated me. I've never had real difficulties with actors. The first days, when I still don't know the people well, I am naturally sometimes unable to find the right approach, to establish an efficient relationship. But this is rare.

You always speak of people, of individuals, instead of

*actors. Do you behave the same way with actors as with other
people and consider them above all as individual human
beings?*

Exactly. I have never decided to use an actor because of
his cleverness or because of his professional abilities, just
as an actor's inexperience has never prevented me from using
him. For my pictures I go in search of expressive faces that
can say everything by themselves when they first appear on
the screen.

I then underline with makeup and costume everything
that might clarify the psychology of the character. The
choice depends on the face that is before me and whatever
I might feel is behind the face, that of someone I usually
don't know, that I've met for the first time. If I make an
error from the beginning—that is, if I attribute to a face a
significance that it doesn't have—I'm usually aware of it at
the first shooting, and I then change the character. I don't
force the actor to take on a guise that is not his; I prefer
to have him express what he can. Most of the time I don't
explain this, to avoid reticence, modesty, or resentment; I
could always say to actors that are in my film: Be yourselves
and don't worry. The result is always positive. Everyone has
the face that suits him; he can't have any other; all faces
are always right—nature doesn't make mistakes.

*Among professional actors, is there any type that you
prefer, with whom you work better than with others?*

I hate actors who reflect upon the character, who arrive
with their ideas and memorize the script. I always try to explain to them that they are wasting time because I always
change all the dialogue—as well as everything else. It
seems to me an unwarranted intrusion. My work with actors
never derives from reasoning, from talks. It is articulated in
a series of commonplace suggestions, taken from observations
of our life in common. One resource for me, in this area, is
to observe the actor when he is not working. At the table,
when he begins to tell his secrets, or discusses politics, or
when he talks to the cameramen. It is there that I see him

as I want to. I often say—it's a phrase that keeps recurring—"Do it the way you did when . . ." And that when might be, for example, an argument with a waiter. I suggest to an actor who has to say, "Get out of this house" to a lover or son, to "Do it the way you did when you told the waiter he had brought you burned rice." Thus I will sometimes have an actor say, "You brought me burned rice" instead of "Get out of this house," and then I fix it during the dubbing.

How do the actors react to this?

At first, some are offended, but then they go along with it. They realize that it might not be worth the trouble to be zealous, to practice their lines in front of a mirror at home. Each time, of course, there's a different rapport, a network of rapports, a number of strings to manipulate. But the cinema is wonderful because of this; it forces you to know people, to understand them and make yourself understood, across psychological barriers, foreign languages, complexes, vanities. Usually, however, the actor who has an ear always knows if the dialogue has the true rhythm on the set.

It is in setting up the situation with the actors, then, that the scene begins to assume its meaning?

For me it's always like that. But I think it's a necessity, a natural characteristic of the cinema. You write pages and pages of dialogue, then you talk a little bit with the set designer and put together a room that says everything. At that point you realize that the dialogue is no longer necessary, that you can say the same things in a more direct, more understandable, more correct way.

For example, the scene I am now shooting, Giorgio's departure from Juliet's home. Excellent dialogue, really very well written, just right. But I ended up shooting the scene so that neither of the characters said a word. She finds him while he is packing his suitcase, she gives him something to eat, and they stand together in silence. At the end

he says, *"Ciao,"* and he leaves her in an unadorned, empty
room, from which I had all the furniture removed.

*When you compare the screenplay with what has been
shot, there really are innumerable changes and variations.
The composition of groups change, such as the friends of
Juliet and Giorgio at the beginning of the film; situations
change; some characters disappear while others appear who
weren't called for in the screenplay.*

I told you, it's always like that. This is a matter of necessity; it is my way of working. The increase in the crowd
is due to the sudden appearance, in my office or around the
set, of faces I think would fit into the picture. No such
character? It doesn't matter. I invent him and put him in.
Other times, I might test someone for an important part;
everything goes well, I tell him he was fine, I compliment
him—and then I change my mind. I find someone else who
is much better. Thus, for the first person, I have to create
another character and make him believe I always thought of
him for that role.

*Why does the grandfather—who among other things is a
very appealing character, a benevolent and protective figure
very different from the gruff and anxious relatives of your
films—why does the grandfather now arrive in an airplane
rather than a balloon?*

You think the grandfather has no precedent? Isn't he a little bit like the Fool in *La Strada?* Affectionate, extravagant,
something of a jester.

I had put the balloon there, but I never liked it. You see
them everywhere now—in newsreels, in household furnishings. It's a symbol that's been used too often; it's really worn
out. I feel somewhat sorry about this balloon. Time was
spent on it from the first day. Fracassi became a specialist
on the subject; he went to Switzerland, he shot a documentary for me on balloons. He warned me of the greatest ca-
tastrophes from the times of Icarus to today. At the end of
this real course of studies, I said: I don't want a balloon

any more, I want a plane. You can imagine how Fracassi looked at me. But the plane is more disturbing, more original, less seen—a kind of large insect. I changed a number of things; I don't even remember the screenplay any more.

Even Susy's arrival at the beach is changed. She no longer arrives in a helicopter, but on a kind of Oriental boat.

It seemed to me right for her to arrive from the water. Also I didn't want the helicopter because it was a reminder of *La Dolce Vita.* Susy couldn't arrive from the sky; ideas come from the sky; she had to come from the water, which is the world of Venus. In the film, Susy is the incarnation of the humiliated femininity of the protagonist. She is shown as an exaggerated, inflated figure—all sex. She's a kind of enchantress of love, a mistress of eroticism. Nothing but a psychological component of Juliet, the other face of the saint on the grating, which represents the masochistic aspect, the satisfaction of frustration. She's a kind of idealization of a pagan divinity, similar to Anitona in *La Dolce Vita* and to the gigantic living photograph in the episode in *Boccaccio '70.* But she's more mischievous, just because as the image of a neglected and repressed aspect of Juliet, she acquires greater strength, more poison.

The Oriental costumes go along with Piero Gherardi's taste; we agreed from the beginning to base them on cartoon figures. I don't have much experience in the field of graphic arts, so I couldn't refer to the work of masters that I don't know well. I suggested to Piero that he create a childlike tone, also a disquieting one, like *Alice in Wonderland.*

I say this above all in reference to the apparitions that follow Juliet and that, at the end, invade her house. The problem was to make them clear on a symbolic level, but of not having them fall into an overwhelming symbolism. I didn't want them to be shown on a neurotic, psychological, scientific level, and I didn't want them to be looked at like the drawings of the insane or the illustrations for an esoteric book of the alchemists. It's fine that something of all that did remain, but in an allusive manner and in the context of an image from a collective unconscious. The more I tried to construct these images with the aid of precise references, the more I realized that the images themselves were being torn to pieces. So I waited for the spirits to appear by themselves, in an experimental panorama. I always shot the realistic sequences first. I tried to have something unexpected or deformed spring out of elements that already existed on the set.

I realize that the film could annoy those who distrust symbols and perhaps delight those who look for symbols everywhere. Although the film lends itself to esoteric, occult, psychoanalytic interpretations, I would like it to be seen in a simpler light: humane and imaginative. Is it a human commentary, enriched by a seductive fantasy? Here, this is the critical problem of the film.

Your collaboration with the scene designer is very important in your films. You start that rather early, don't you?

Piero Gherardi, who has done all my recent films, and I have the same basic tastes, and because of this we are in agreement. The work with Piero, the passing around of drawings and sketches, usually begins a little before abandoning the screenplay. By the time I open the office, I am already in daily contact with Gherardi, just because I have decided to look the film in the eye. From that moment on, as we gather together indications day by day from the people we see, from the places we visit, the figurative aspect of the film too begins to take shape, more and more precisely. For *Juliet of the Spirits* I want to congratulate Piero with more warmth than usual. He was *bravissimo*.

Do you consider your relationship with the cameraman a very important one?

From the moment the shooting of the film begins, it is essential, just as is the relationship with the set designer during the preparatory stages. The wrong lighting on a scene is like a sentence with adjectives out of order. The cameraman is a hand of the director that technically assures him of certain results. The best cameraman for my films is the one who follows me—even hesitating—and does what I ask of him. It's better if he's intelligent, of course; intelligence is never wasted. I mean only that I prefer an eclectic cameraman to one with positive tastes. I need one who understands my demands and knows how to translate them with irreproachable skill. I have worked very well with Gianni di Venanzo in *8½* and in *Juliet* as in the past I did with the excellent Martelli.

Your camera is quite mobile; it tends to embrace its subjects with angles up to 360 degrees, which calls for acrobatic lighting. Do you think that this extreme mobility is the stylistic equivalent, the portrait of your attitude of eternal curiosity?

The camera in my films is not always moving; it depends on what I am telling. I believe I have the internal rhythm of the sequences in mind well before shooting begins. In this I am very faithful to my first conceptions; when I begin to see a scene in a certain way, I make no more changes. In any case, I have never made decisions about style, only attempted to make myself carry out a meaning expressed in determined cadences. If I find that a scene assumes a significance because the camera has started rolling around a glass and goes on to the discovery of all the rest, I adjust my way of shooting to the discovery I have made.

Do you think of the music after the cutting, as is usually done?

Music comes into my films by means of records while I'm shooting. Themes that have been in my mind for years ("Titina," "The March of the Gladiators"), tied to precise emotions, visceral themes. And then records that I hear by chance, like "Patricia," which I heard in a bar at Tor Vaianica, on the juke box; that became the theme of *La Dolce Vita*. I put it in at the time of the rehearsals, and it became a great stimulus, a spring. As you know, the composer for all my films has been Nino Rota, a man made of music, an angelic friend.

This time Nino wrote the music ahead of time, because it seemed that the film had to come out before expected. Usually his work begins at the end of the cutting, though sometimes I advance this while I'm still shooting. I asked him not to write movie music and not to use a connecting theme. They are all different themes, in the guise of chamber music, with few instruments: seventeenth- or eighteenth-century airs, a little Mozartian, with titles like "The Pine Forest" and "A Day at the Sea." They could be played at a concert. They seem to me of an enchanting grace, very elegant, in addition to being filled with the happy immediacy of everything that Nino has written.

In your films you have always shown a predilection for the story told in "chapters." This kind of fragmentation is already evident in The White Sheik, *which tells a story over a period of twenty-four hours. In* I Vitelloni *and* La Strada, *this is shown in the passing of seasons: there are summer chapters, autumn chapters, winter chapters.* Il Bidone *is a step forward toward an even more open expression, while* The Nights of Cabiria *almost calls for little titles for the various episodes that make up the portrait of the protagonist. For* La Dolce Vita, *you effected what you yourself called, during the writing of the screenplay, "a Picasso noncomposition." I remember your saying you wanted to create a sculpture, break it into pieces and then examine the pieces one by one. You did it even better in* 8½, *where the story in a traditional sense is absorbed by other things; it really tends to disappear. I have the feeling that this too happens with* Juliet of the Spirits. *Has this tendency away from a tight form and toward a broader, less definable expression any significance?*

I don't really know; it hasn't been a voluntary process. I don't think I have ever set out with the decision to choose a certain form of story. It has always been the subject that has determined the proper solution for me. I have always started off in love with a character, a landscape, a climate. Perhaps more in a lyrical key than a narrative one. The slightly rhapsodic tone you speak of probably derives from this—

the story told in chapters, in little pictures, like the ancient frescos or cartoon strips. The strange thing is that the tight, rigid construction of directors like Hitchcock has always fascinated me; I would very much like to be able to do a film one day that is as neat and precise as the design of a crystal. I would have to impose a discipline upon myself, as an exercise. Get away for once from the charms of a story told in sweeping cadences, enclose everything in a perfect geometry.

A few weeks before starting Juliet of the Spirits, *you spoke to me in just these terms: a film that should have the precise design of a crystal.*

A precise story reflected in so many mirrors. I certainly would have liked to do the film this way; maybe even a little of it is like that. I thought about it, but then I forgot. Now I don't know. From the contemplation of disorder to the love of geometry: too good to be true.

In this rather free structure of your films, have you had any literary models in mind? Speaking of your latest films, critics have referred to Joyce, Proust, Mann, and Musil. I myself, speaking of 8½, *found comparisons with* The Confessions of Zeno *by Italo Svevo—as a confession by proxy, a story that involves the entire life of a man from the womb up to the mystery that surrounds his death.*

I'm sorry, but I've always found that kind of question useless. I could answer, as usual, that I haven't read anything. It would only be partially true, but enough so. There are books that have fascinated me: Kafka, for example, and even before, Dostoyevsky. And then *Orlando Furioso, The Thousand and One Nights, Gulliver's Travels, Don Quixote.* But in general I'm not a reader of authors, of poets. I do strange, curious reading. I like to read newspapers, the minutes of a trial. I don't have much interest in writers who offer me their own worlds; I prefer scientific manuals, history books, a few pages of philosophy. Even when I don't understand everything, this seems to be enriching. Don't make me say that I haven't read Joyce, because I'm ashamed. I can see the faces of Moravia and Pasolini, judging me affectionately, but full of reservations and a little amused. No, I refuse to proclaim my ignorance. In addition, it would be antieducational. Should we teach young people that it's only worthwhile to read comic strips?

The truth is that it isn't necessary to read a certain author —say, Joyce—if Joyce has really been important, as he has been, to contemporary culture. Then you come to know Joyce by looking at the layout of a magazine, speaking with people, observing how a girl is dressed.

It is, of course, better to read and to understand everything, as Pasolino and Brunello Rondi do. But culture, when it is authentic and has a profound effect, doesn't spare the ignorant, the lazy, the unprepared. I would say that the true cultural facts are breathed in the air, become sets, perspectives in a city, keys to your private relationships. The life we will live tomorrow can be anticipated today more than described by every true poet. And so how can I tell you that all those writers you named didn't influence me at all, that I don't know them well enough, that I am a narrator of very private stories?

As a narrator of private stories, you enjoy a privilege that is becoming more and more rare: Your ideas and thoughts, if we can thus define your films, interest a vast public, from New York to Moscow. They are compared to and stand with the most advanced expressions of contemporary art. And, at the same time, they excite the public. If yours is an avant-garde cinema, using the term in the sense of experimental, don't you think that your success derives from the fact that you bring back, with new dimensions, the traditional elements, such as psychology, intrigues, and suspense, thus avoiding the boredom that is the mortal enemy of the art of today?

The cinema, you see, is a curious phenomenon. I just saw *Goldfinger*, a film that impressed me very much. Beyond the enameled surface, the brilliant mixture of adventure, told very well, I feel that there is a world of beetles, terrible, anguished. It seems to me one of those films that moves the cinema a step forward, in spite of my reservations for the discomfort it causes me. I don't know if I'm explaining myself. It succeeds in capturing, within a conventional form, the message of the man of today—even if partial, distorted, mad. And it is because of this that I think the film has had such a great success with the public.

Is your rapport with the public important to you? Or do you consider it only as a practical matter? You are one of the few artists who succeed in reconciling your personal style with that of the entertainment itself. La Dolce Vita *is not* Goldfinger—*it is a handmade product, not one created in a laboratory—yet it has raised considerable interest. How do you explain this? Is it a gift, or luck? Or is it the result of a constant search for the reactions that your work might cause in a theater? When you work and invent, do you think of the spectator? And which? Italian? Foreign? Today's? Tomorrow's? In other words, for whom do you work?*

This "meeting" with the public is a gift, an almost clown-like calling, à la Barnum or Buffalo Bill. The factor of communicating is unconscious. I've never considered for a moment whether the public will understand or not. The public is an abstract entity; one cannot foresee what it will do. The captivating quality (some might call it pandering) that you find in my pictures, if it is there, is completely instinctive.

So if a film of yours was not understood, would it be a crisis for you, or would you say, "Too bad for them?"

Let's get away from generalities and come to specific cases. Things that have happened. I am a director whose scripts are always—when I say always I mean always—rejected by producers. Even those who receive me respectfully, with friendship, with affection, invariably say to me, "This film won't make a lira; it's not cinema, it's half literature; it's something that will interest four cats; why don't you do a book?" Each time I have told my ideas to those who were to produce them, in the presence of experts and specialists, it ended in smiles, maybe because I am good enough at putting on these little shows, but only in a congenial atmosphere. You say, *if* a picture of mine wasn't understood? *Variety Lights* was a fiasco; *The White Sheik* an enormous fiasco, the worst of 1950. Nobody wanted to distribute *I Vitelloni*—we went around begging for rentals like desperate men. I remember some terrifying screenings. Those present, at the end, cast oblique looks at me and mournfully shook hands with Pegoraro, the producer. I don't remember the names, and even if I did, it's best not to mention them.

I remember one screening, at two o'clock on a summer's afternoon, for the president of a huge company. He came in buoyantly, bronzed from the rays of a sun lamp, with a gold chain on his wrist, like an automobile salesman, the type women like. We sat ourselves in a very comfortable little room, all colored, the interior of a piece of hard candy. He insisted that Pegoraro and I do as he did and put our feet up on the chairs in front of us—a very uncomfortable position. The film began, and he, telephone at his side, started to make little calls—"How goes it? . . . What did you eat? . . . Come later, for that we'll see. . . ." Then there was a knock and two porters came in with an enormous statue, a nude woman, and he said to me, "You are an artist; tell me if you like it." The statue was taken away and the secretary arrived with the mail. Suddenly the film seemed to interest this potential distributor, but he only wanted to know what kind of car my brother Riccardo was driving in the film. In a loud voice he then told of the life and miracles of that model. Finally the film ended and we got up. He went out first, with Pegoraro behind him; they went down the corridor. I heard him say, "What can I say, there isn't . . . I don't think . . ." and he made a gesture with his hand.

He didn't take it. It ended up with another distributor who didn't want the title *I Vitelloni*. He suggested *Vagabonds!,* with an exclamation point. I said that was fine, but to make it even stronger we had to have the voice of an ogre shouting *Vagabonds!* along with the written title. They accepted the title when Pegoraro gave them two other pictures they considered commercial. But they didn't want Alberto Sordi's name on the posters and billboards—"He'll make people run away, the public can't stand him." I tell you all this to show that the approval or disapproval of the surroundings, and eventually that of the public, doesn't worry me very much. I have sometimes said, and I think honestly, that when a film is finished, it would be the same for me even if it never came out.

Don't you think this is a proud attitude?

I don't know. Let me think. I want to try to understand. Presumptuous, maybe. But I don't think so. The man who feeds on doubts rarely becomes presumptuous. I would say it's a matter of a good conscience. Yes, just the fact of saying that I can't do more than this. Considering my laziness, my weakness, the confusion—in other words, given the kind of person I am—I couldn't do any better.

I don't know how I'd react if there were repeated failures. Basically, apart from *The White Sheik,* there are no symptomatic episodes. That time—but I was much younger than I am now—the disaster stimulated me, the goading and the meanness of the criticism made me become aggressive, mocking. All in all, out of it came a kind of positive resentment. This is a side of my character that comes from Romagna. The man who has been laughed at goes arrogantly ahead.

After all that we have said, though you are opposed to theorization and generalities, I would like to ask you if you feel the distinction between films based on one's own stories and those based on the stories of others is legitimate. That is, is this distinction the same as that between author and director? Or do you feel that even for the director who hasn't written his own script there is enough creative scope in the making of the film?

If we talk about my own case, I have to say—with all gratitude to those who work with me—that I consider myself father and mother of my films. I am helped by knowledgeable obstetricians and faithful friends, but the conception is mine alone.

As to whether to have these ideas or not, whether to write or not, I'll let you, as a critic, answer that. Personally, I feel there's a misunderstanding in all this. However, it would be interesting to use someone else's script, thought of and completely written by someone else, to make—every once in a while—a film that starts from a more concrete base and not from the usual chaos in which I try to put some order. It would be good for me. By nature I am led to appreciate a cinema that is staffed by capable people, who know their work and do it with humility; their commitment is more understandable than the impulsive inspirations of a lot of self-styled artists.

I repeat that I would, once, like to show that glass as it is. Not how I see it, but how it is. A clear, well-organized film, written by others.

GIULIETTA

Juliet of the Spirits *is a film that revolves around a woman, as have the others*—La Strada *and* The Nights of Cabiria—*that you made with Giulietta Masina as the star. Carl Gustav Jung, in a 1927 lecture on "The Woman in Europe," said: "Can a man be capable of writing about a woman, his opposite? I mean writing something true and fair, beyond every sexual concept or resentment, beyond any illusion or theory. I really don't know who could assume such a superiority; the woman stands, in fact, in the shadow of the man, so that too often he confuses the woman with his own shadow; and every once in a while he tries to repair this misunderstanding by overevaluating the woman and attributing to her his desires. I am thus prepared to examine this theme with the broadest reservations."*

This seems to me very true! To undertake to speak calmly and clearly about a woman is almost impossible for a man. If I have faced this and continue to face it, it is because a storyteller has the right to speak about everything, regardless of his inadequacy. It could also be forbidden, by the same token, to talk about flowers, trees, and nature—vital dimensions that we can't capture in their genuine essence. All the same, we do speak about them, aware that in certain areas we are still at the first letters of the alphabet.

It is a little difficult, and perhaps even indiscreet, to ask you what Giulietta represents in your life after twenty-two years of marriage in a world in which marriages generally last a shorter time. It seems to me that you, quite willing to speak about yourself and your business, go into this theme far less willingly. However, between you and Giulietta there is a rapport in life and art that goes back to the time of Variety Lights; *and even before that, the character of Giulietta in* Senza Pietà *was written by you. Then came your most famous films, not even counting the appearances of Giulietta in* The White Sheik *and* Il Bidone. *I would like to ask you if this collaboration has a practical meaning— that is, the necessity or the opportunity of writing roles for Giulietta—or if it goes beyond that.*

I've always considered the meeting with Giulietta to be a meeting of destiny; it doesn't seem to me that things could have gone any other way. This is a longtime rapport that I would consider preexistent to the day on which it was verified. It was at the radio station, as has been told many times, where Giulietta was reading some little scenes that I had written. Our work relationship is parallel to the other, and it has always been that way. But I don't believe I've ever worked with Giulietta out of necessity or mere opportunity. Our life together is, logically, a fountain of continual observation. I will say that she is the kind of actress who fits in very well with my intentions, my taste: her face, her postures, her expressions, her tones. Giulietta is an actress of mimicry, of cadences, of clownishness. But she is also a person of sufficient mystery who can embody, in relationship to me, a consuming nostalgia for innocence, for perfection.

There are obviously similarities between Giulietta herself and the roles Giulietta plays—Gelsomina, Cabiria, Juliet. Which do you think is the character that she resembles the most?

Giulietta as an actress would like to be the opposite of the person that she is with me. Every time, she is hesitant, she gives in after much resistance, as if she didn't want to give life to something dark that is in her and that she rejects. In the beginning she hates the clothing, the expressions, the masks of her characters. Right next to the enthusiastic, hard-working Giulietta, a partner, there seems to appear another Giulietta who says no.

This latest film seems to me to deal with the character that best represents Giulietta, in which she assumes a concrete form. At the beginning it was a serious problem to remove—not from her, from me—the smiles, the pallor, the winks of a lost puppy that she assumed in the roles of Gelsomina and Cabiria; the roles that grew inside of me and finally were superimposed on her, in terms of cinema. The job of removing these without completely erasing them, that is, salvaging those features of Gelsomina and Cabiria that exist in Giulietta herself—this was painful! At a certain point, I thought I couldn't do it, so much so that I kept putting off the most vital and revealing scenes till the last. Then, one fine day, I made a discovery. Giulietta's resistance to the makeup, clothing, hairdo, earrings, her firm stands that other times seemed to me crimes against the character, intolerable interventions of femininity—this time they were functional. I shouldn't have become angry, because the Giulietta of this film was right to act this way, to show these aggressions. Questioning the details of her clothing, Giulietta worked with me and helped me. When she complained about her makeup or when she fought with Gherardi about a dress, I should have carefully watched her attitude as an actress with understanding, because the healthy side of the character was contained in this very attitude.

Gelsomina and Cabiria belonged to the world of the proletariat; Juliet is a middle-class woman with other experiences and dimensions in her life, one more closely related to Giulietta herself. Is it because of this that you think the character resembles her the most?

Perhaps this too. But above all because in this film there

has been much more collaboration between Giulietta and myself. From my point of view it was easy. A number of times, on the spur of the moment, I just asked Giulietta what she would say, what she would do; and I accepted her solutions without the slightest change.

Was this film born as a film about Giulietta or is it a case of an idea to which the actress was drawn later on?

It was born as a film about Giulietta and for Giulietta. There was a very long period of gestation, going back to *La Strada*. More than the desire to make another picture with Giulietta, I felt that my desire to use the cinema as an instrument to penetrate certain areas of reality could find the perfect guide in Giulietta. The germination of the idea was lost in the last years, in my search for a theme that—even more than the story of Gelsomina—would lend itself to describing a different reality. There had been the idea of a film about a nun whose diary we found in a convent library while we were shooting *La Strada*. A very sweet, unknown provincial saint. But there was the danger of falling into a pastel mysticism, an ecstatic hagiography.

Juliet of the Spirits *is even the destruction of a certain type of hagiography. I am thinking of the scene in the nuns' little theater, when the recitation is so forcefully interrupted by the grandfather.*

Of course. But with a less astonishing, less enrapturing point of view: It is a little like the film about the nun transferred to an objective level. I also tried to put together these interests of mine around the character of Eileen Garrett, the medium, whom I knew. Her autobiography seemed to me, for a while, a promising starting point for a film. We didn't go ahead in that direction, probably because of my inability to tell a life story, that is, to obligate myself to tell it faithfully, which would have tied my hands from the very beginning. And then, the life of such a woman, with all the inherent difficulties—to show something, or not show it . . .

later there was another project, always in the same key, always with Giulietta. I wanted to give her a chance to play many roles in one film—a soapmaker, a strong, miserly woman, a fortuneteller, a millionairess. Old, discarded projects that I was for a while tempted to put together in one story. I had even found the thread between them, but then nothing was done about it.

After 8½, feeling it was time to make another film with Giulietta, I tried to get going, in a different perspective, on my old desire. It is probably directed to the screen in many dimensions. The idea of making a film about the invisible world is postponed; at present, it is perhaps not possible. However, I have been impelled by a psychological point of view that allows for a wide margin of detachment, irony, and entertainment, and that in addition to judgment can contain the most unrestrained fantasy.

The apparitions in the film have the same substance as the real characters, and vice versa. Indeed, sometimes more than one character is presented suddenly with a completely unreal look, so much so that a stimulating ambiguity between fantasy and reality is created.

The ambiguity is intentional and is one of the keys to the film. The thing that really made it effective was the color— it was a very important element. It is the color that determines the ambiguity between the trickiness and the fantastic lighting.

On the set, is your relationship with Giulietta a professional one, that of actress and director? That is, do you direct Giulietta in a special way or as you do the others? Are there habits, subtleties, understandings that you carry from one film to another?

I am more nervous, more exacting with Giulietta than with the others. I can tolerate the errors of others; those of Giulietta trouble me. In this I am very unfair. The fact is that Giulietta lives within me so much more than the other actors; it seems to me that she hasn't the right to make mistakes. Sometimes I would like to say to her: "How is it, you were born in this story before everything, and you still don't feel perfectly integrated to the image that we are putting together?"

When we speak of work off the set, she is often argumentative, has her own ideas, raises various objections. But in front of the camera she is very docile and completely obedient. Giulietta is very good; she does everything possible to make things easy for me. And she never stops being the wife. She comes over to ask if I'm cold, if my shoes are wet, if I want coffee. . . .

THE MARRIED WOMAN

It seems to me that the critics haven't adequately noted the importance in your films that the theme of marriage assumes; the relationship of a man and woman here and now. Variety Lights *was the story of a restless husband and a patient wife.* The White Sheik *was a fable built around a mistaken marriage between an ingenuous little wife and a pretentious boor. One of the connecting threads of* I Vitelloni *was a marriage between two immature young people. In the episode* The Matrimonial Agency *in* Love in the City, *a girl was willing to marry a werewolf in order to get settled.* La Strada *has always seemed to me a metaphor of Italian marriage; the surly, domineering, weak man; the woman unaware of her own strength and her own equality, sensitive, inspired. Even in* Il Bidone, *there is a marriage based on a lie. In* The Nights of Cabiria, *the poor prostitutes aspire to marriage to put their lives in order. In* La Dolce Vita, *the tie between Marcello and Emma, even if they're not married, is visceral, violent, and unbearable, like an old marriage that has gone bad. In that film, too, in the tragedy of Steiner who kills his children and himself, the ambiguity and hardships of an apparently serene marriage are clearly suggested.* 8½ *is a story of yesterday, and it represents a reevaluation of the figure of the wife as an effective foundation in a chaotic, confused world, difficult to interpret and to bear.* Juliet of the Spirits, *in spite of evolving in a fantastic element, is the story of a matrimonial crisis. We have now named, with the exception of the episode in* Boccaccio '70, *which has a precise satiric objective, all of your films. Why do you think you have emphasized the theme of marriage so much?*

Because I think that for us Italians marriage is still one of the fundamental experiences. From the time we were children, they've accustomed us to the fable that ends: "They married and lived happily ever after." It's a kind of goal they've put in our heads, one we must inevitably face. It's a point of arrival in life, not a point of departure—the end and not the beginning, both for the man and the woman. The error of a certain type of education is all there: exchanging the first chapter of a book for the conclusion of the book. The majority of people come to marriage completely unprepared because this event has been made into a myth, told in an inexact and treacherous manner. It becomes a catalyst of disillusionment, of tragic thoughts, of neurosis.

In my films, I have spoken about marriage because it is one of the things we know the best. There is something eternal, necessary, in the union of two human beings. But the way it's considered today, it is more the legalization, the recognition of certain obscure tendencies. To sum it up, I don't believe that marriage is what it is superficially thought to be, and I am certain that it is a matter of far deeper rapport. Thus, in my films I have called attention to the degeneration, the caricature of this rapport, which is uncertain, the most uncertain thing of all. It is profoundly individual. It can't be regulated by collective standards, by customs imposed from the outside, by various taboos. Giving into marriage easily should be forbidden. So many of us succumb passively to the laws of nature, which have been deformed by current usage, let ourselves be sucked in and swallowed up by marriage, completely overlooking its highest—and only —purpose: the attempt to realize a true union.

In Juliet of the Spirits *I seem to find once again the dialects of* La Strada, *brought up to date. The husband, Giorgio, who puts a black mask over his eyes and plugs in his ears in order to sleep, who neither sees nor hears—isn't he a modern Zampanò in the guise of a public relations man? And isn't Juliet a middle-class Gelsomina, a child surrounded by adults who don't understand, a person of good sense who shows us ways still unlearned through knowledge?*

When I made *La Strada*, I was not thinking of marriage. The point of departure of that film, apart from the spectacle of nature and the fascination of the gypsylike travels, was the story of an enlightenment, of the shaking of a conscience, through the sacrifice of another creature.

I remember that you told me many years ago, right after La Strada *came out, that you considered the relationship between Zampanò and Gelsomina to be an unreal situation, saying: "But three-quarters of Italian marriages are like that. The husband comes home and doesn't speak; the wife lowers her eyes." In the film this situation is perfectly delineated—naturally under the cover of a fable.*

Maybe you're right. *La Strada* is still the film that represents my shadowy areas; I am certainly not capable of drawing from it the meanings that you find. Whether *Juliet* represents the continuation of that theme, as you believe, I just don't know. . . .

It seems to me, too, that there is a development, a strengthening of your matrimonial theme. For the solution of Gelsomina, as a kind of bewitched victim stemming perhaps from a traditional mysticism, in Juliet of the Spirits *you substitute a knowledge of oneself and of others that, among your other films, appears only in* 8½. *You seem to invite the character, the woman, to take stock of her own being and her own possibilities.*

I feel instinctively that it is right and opportune to go into this matter and a good time to do it. I am not sure, however, that I myself am clear enough about it to go into it fairly. One could see the film and conclude that it says that wives should not give their husbands a bad time of it. But at the same time, one can reverse that; one can say by the same token that husbands should not oppress their wives, consider them private property, place them in slavery without real love. I am thinking of Jung's observation on the difficulties of a man writing about women, and I wonder if I was honest, if I didn't idealize the woman in order to remove her from the contest of masculine interests.

The intention of the film, from this point of view, is to restore to the woman her true independence, her indisputable and inalienable dignity. A free man, I mean, cannot do without a free woman. The wife must not be the Madonna, nor an instrument of pleasure, and least of all a servant. If we consider the wife, even for a moment, under one of these three aspects, we will find we are not speaking of a marriage, but of something else—and always to our disadvantage.

Maybe *Juliet of the Spirits* is still not the honest, exhaustive, complete treatment that one can make of this subject. Perhaps it doesn't even succeed in stating half the truth, but it tries to do so. In any case, the problem is everyone's; to put it off is useless and damaging. The independence of women is the theme of the future. Not, of course, in terms of the suffragettes, of the campaigns for emancipation of women.

On this point, too, you agree with Jung when he writes that man must live as a man and woman as a woman.

The masculinization of the woman is one of the most horrible things possible. No, woman mustn't emancipate herself for imitation—which would be a development within the projection of that famous masculine shadow—but to discover her own reality, a different one. Different, it seems to me, from that of the man, but profoundly complementary and integral to it. It would be a step toward a happier humanity.

Going through Jung's writings, I found another passage that seems to apply to the situation in Juliet of the Spirits:

"Woman feels that marriage no longer offers her complete security. In fact, what purpose does the husband's fidelity serve, if she knows that his feelings and thoughts are absent from it and that he is merely too reasonable or cowardly to follow them? What purpose does her own fidelity serve when she knows that with it she is only paying for his right of possession and that her soul is decaying in the process? She intuitively perceives a greater fidelity, in the spirit and love, beyond weaknesses and human imperfections."

To demand from others a fidelity to ourselves is monstrous; it is an antireligious thought. The only true fidelity is to oneself and to one's own destiny, absolutely respecting each one's individuality. How could it be otherwise? I know that the present moral current, our laws, all our daily living, are often founded on contrary concepts, but I have absolutely no doubt that this must change.

Critics have often complained that you end your films in a vague, general way: Cabiria's appeal to hope, the reminder of the purity of the little girl in La Dolce Vita. *It seems to me that in* Juliet of the Spirits, *no one can say that you have avoided a conclusive summary of your intentions. As happened, too, in 8½.*

This is one of the criticisms that I've never understood, for as far as I'm concerned the public writes the ending. The storyteller shouldn't say, "Here the story ends," if he doesn't want his story to be reduced to the level of a pastime, an anecdote, a joke. If the story has moved you, the ending is up to you, who have seen it.

Juliet alone, at the end of the film, should mean the discovery of an individuality. The thing she feared the most, the departure of her husband, is revealed as a gift of providence. Juliet will no longer depend on the paternal figure of Giorgio, who has, nonetheless, enriched her life. To him, too, as to everyone and everything, Juliet feels grateful because they all—even those who seem the most fearful enemies—helped the process of her liberation. In the end, Juliet's

real life begins when she comes out of the shadow of
Giorgio.

   *The opposite of "They lived happily ever after." Not a con-
clusion, but a beginning.*

PART TWO

JULIET OF THE SPIRITS

Original Screenplay

This screenplay, which attempts to convey, if only roughly, the feeling of the film, was valuable to me as a series of provisional notes from which to begin the preparation and organization of the film itself.

As is my habit, while the preparatory work proceeded I retained the right to revise, to specify changes and substitute scenes and characters, to enrich situations, to set the pace of the film as well as the dialogue and atmosphere—sometimes comic, sometimes anguished, sometimes shocking—of the story.

It is important for me to state clearly that the film must be a total stylistic reconstruction of reality, in order to obtain particular shadings of color; just as the characters must find through appropriate costumes a distinct and unequivocal definition.

—FEDERICO FELLINI

JULIET OF THE SPIRITS

The Screenplay

THE PINE FOREST OF FREGENE, AND JULIET'S HOME.
EXTERIOR. DAYTIME. (SUNSET.)

The slanting rays of the sun as it sets across the pines of Fregene. The quiet houses, almost all closed, in the uncertain, enchanted light of the hour.

Among these small villas, one: Juliet's. The small trees in the garden, the green grass, the waiting cats, the flowers in the flower beds: everything stopped, immobile, as in a child's drawing.

Light can be seen through the windows and through one, at intervals, the shape of a woman moving quickly and happily through the house.

JULIET'S HOME. INTERIOR. DAYTIME. (SUNSET.)

Juliet, in a cocktail dress, wearing a little jewelry and already made up, is putting the finishing touches to her makeup and to her hair in front of the large bathroom mirror. She looks at herself carefully—from the front, the side, from every angle. She raises and then lowers a lock of hair, adjusts her lipstick a bit, but she is obviously in a hurry, calling out every once in a while, gaily.

JULIET: Fortunata! (*No one answers. Juliet runs the comb through her hair again, gives a last hurried but careful look at herself in the mirror, and calls out again.*) Fortunata!

She goes out of the bathroom quickly and into the kitchen, where she finds Fortunata ready to leave, pocketbook and bundles in hand.

> FORTUNATA: I put everything out, signora. . . . The champagne is in the refrigerator . . . so is the salad and the mayonnaise. Now I'm going. Good night, signora.

Juliet checks the dish cooking in the oven, then opens the refrigerator, puts the champagne in a bucket and quickly grabs a cat who tries to jump into the refrigerator.

> JULIET: Go on, get out. What nerve! (*No sooner does she get this cat out of the kitchen than a second one very quickly pushes through the door and under the table.*) Fortunata! Grab Tiresia. Gently, because she's blind. (*To the cats*) You've all eaten; now all cats out of this house! (*Fortunata succeeds in grabbing the big black cat and throwing him out of the door, at the same time making sure that no others come in. Juliet, in the meantime, takes the dessert out of the refrigerator so that it doesn't get too cold.*) See you tomorrow, Fortunata. Thank you. Oh, the candles—
> FORTUNATA: I put them in, signora. The red ones.

Juliet, without responding, goes to see if the table is properly set. Here, too, everything is in order. The table is set "elegantly," as seen in women's magazines, for an intimate dinner. A colored tablecloth, a large silver candelabra with four candles in the center. While Juliet looks for matches and lights the candles, Fortunata looks in through the kitchen door and repeats that she is leaving, good night. Nevertheless, she stays a moment to see the effect of the lighted candles on the table. Juliet turns off the overhead light and the small lamps in the room. Everything breathes intimacy, and what elegance! With a final, rather unconvincing good night, Fortunata leaves. Juliet runs to the kitchen to get the champagne bucket. She hears the sound of the horn announcing the arrival of her husband. She rushes to the mirror for one final look, then returns to the kitchen for the champagne bucket; she joyously enters the living room to receive her husband's praises for a lovely surprise.

Her husband, Giorgio, an elegant, handsome, worldly man, is on the threshold watching her gravely. He notices that the lights are out; he doesn't understand.

> GIORGIO: What's wrong? Did the lights go out? (*He turns the switch; the light comes on. He looks questioningly at Juliet, who is obviously upset.*) Well, is it your birth—? Of course not. Mine? (*He laughs, enjoying himself, and goes on.*) You know, you had a good idea? I didn't even warn you! Look who's here—Valentina and Raniero have made peace again.

Giorgio turns Juliet toward the garden and points out.

JULIET'S GARDEN. EXTERIOR. DAYTIME. (SUNSET.)

A group of people standing, waiting on the lawn: Valentina with her lover, Raniero; Alba, a painter, and Chierichetta, a young homosexual who acts as both model and confidante to Alba. The latter limps slightly, leaning on a cane. As soon as Juliet appears at the entrance to the garden, the group moves, coming toward the house, shouting their greetings.

JULIET'S HOME. INTERIOR. DAYTIME. (SUNSET.)

Valentina, Raniero, Alba, and Chierichetta enter the living room, invading it and scattering themselves throughout the house. Valentina and Raniero, somewhat comically, underscore their eternal love by stealing kisses and holding each other tightly. Alba talks in a high voice, occasionally bursting into hysterical laughter. Chierichetta waddles all over the place.

> VALENTINA: My love . . . Dear, did you see Raniero? He came back last night.
> ALBA: I fell down, imagine. I was setting up the easel, and it fell right on me.

VALENTINA (*whispering to Juliet*): It was Romoletto. A
little more and he would have beaten her to death.

Chierichetta is heading for the bathroom. Alba goes toward the kitchen.

CHIERICHETTA: Where's the bathroom? It's so beautiful
here. Oh, God, my hands are dirty! How awful.
GIORGIO: Do we have enough food for everyone, or
should I get something at the store?
JULIET: No, no. There's enough. I'll fix it. Sit down.
ALBA (*entering the kitchen, shouting loudly*): I'll do it.
I'll do it. I'll make you a Hungarian pilaf. Is there any
paprika?

Valentina stands looking at the table set for two. She suddenly puts her arms around Juliet, who is going toward Alba
in the kitchen.

VALENTINA: Oh, God. How beautiful! How enchanting!
It makes me heartsick.

Giorgio is going up the stairs with Raniero; he is showing
him the house.

RANIERO: And upstairs? How many rooms?

Before entering the kitchen, Juliet turns to Giorgio and
Raniero, a little disturbed:

JULIET: But where are you going? Everything upstairs
is . . .

She goes to the kitchen, where Alba has already opened
the refrigerator, the cupboard, the oven, etc. She is ran-
sacking eveywhere, singing a song of her own invention.

ALBA: Paprika, paprika, paprika, paprika . . . there is no
paprika. (*To Juliet*) Darling, go away. I don't want to
see you in here. I'll take care of everything. Painting,
cooking, making love—my calling. Today the only

thing missing has been the cooking. (*She starts her vulgar laughter again and pushes Juliet away.*) Out, out, out.

Pushed by Alba, Juliet goes to the bedroom, meeting Chierichetta, who is coming out of the bathroom drying his hands and face.

CHIERICHETTA: Excuse me, Juliet, but your soap really won't do. It has an odor that's—excuse me—nauseating. I can't get rid of it.

He goes to the living room.

Juliet goes to the bathroom and shuts herself in. She stares silently in front of the mirror while the voices and laughter of the unexpected guests resound through the house. She does her best to hold back the tears. Looking at her own image in the mirror, she mumbles.

JULIET: Now, don't be a fool. Don't start to cry.

But she is almost crying. She is startled and stops herself because the door is opened by Valentina, who enters carrying a lighted incense stick. Deeply absorbed, Valentina passes the stick repeatedly under Juliet's nose.

VALENTINA: Look what I brought. (*She leans lightly on Juliet, looking at herself in the mirror.*) Touch my hands. They're frozen. I feel a presence all around. This place . . . these plants . . . I'm constantly receiving this evening. I feel new entities. . . . I feel them physically.

Someone tries to enter the bathroom; it is Giorgio, who, finding it closed, calls out.

GIORGIO'S VOICE: Who's there?
JULIET: I . . . we're coming right away.

She fixes herself up while Valentina says:

VALENTINA: We're coming. We're coming.

Giorgio tries to open the door again.

GIORGIO'S VOICE: But what are you doing in there?

Juliet has finished pulling herself together and opens the door, leaving with Valentina. As soon as she comes out, she finds herself in front of Giorgio. Valentina goes to the living room; from there is heard the sound of a phonograph. Giorgio, upset, feeling a little guilty, looks at Juliet and asks:

GIORGIO: What's wrong? Are you all right?
JULIET: Of course. Nothing's wrong. I'm fine.
GIORGIO: You know, I couldn't help it.
JULIET: Of course, of course. You did the right thing. A good idea. (*Suddenly*) Do you love me?

Giorgio smiles, reassured, kisses her on the cheek. He takes her by the arm and leads her to the living room. In the room, Chierichetta is dancing to the sound of the phonograph.

DISSOLVE

Supper is finished. The room is now lighted only by candlelight. Juliet, Alba, Chierichetta, and Raniero, intense and serious, are seated around a three-legged table. Giorgio is stretched out in an armchair, a note pad on his knees and a pencil in hand. On the phonograph, a record of the Beatles.
Valentina, tense, her eyes sparkling, moves about in the semidarkness, silently and rapidly as a shadow. She sees a cat in the room and puts it out in the garden; the cat immediately reappears on the window ledge. She takes a candle and with it lights a stick of incense, which she then passes around Giorgio's head three times. She speaks softly, inspired.

VALENTINA: Cats, no. They attract restless spirits. Giorgio, you're staying out? Good. You transcribe the messages. Maybe the other chair was better. You must always make a triangle. It doesn't matter; don't move now. You've already filled that corner with fluid. (*She approaches those seated around the table and passes the incense stick three times around the head of each one.*) My God, how many presences! They're all around here already. But tonight there's a new one—one that's never come here before. (*She bends down toward Juliet and whispers to her as to an accomplice*). It wants to communicate with one of us. It must say something. (*Eyes wide open, Juliet looks at her—with hope, diffidence, and fright. But now Valentina tosses back her hair and smiles at Juliet absentmindedly, one eye looking right, the other left, like the eyes of Venus. She mumbles softly with the voice of a promise that seems almost lascivious.*) Concentrate. (*She inserts the incense stick in a chrysanthemum, letting a thin thread of smoke develop. Then she takes her place in the circle, placing her long hands on the table in contact with the hands of the others.*) Don't think of anything. Empty your insides.

But the incense stick is right behind Juliet, the chrysanthemum lightly touching her face, so that her eyes tear from the smoke and her nose begins to itch. She sneezes with a jerk that makes the chain break.

JULIET: It's the smoke. Excuse me.

They all raise their heads and look at her. Juliet, lowering her face, closes her eyes and concentrates again—with zeal and absolute fanaticism. The hands on the table come close to each other, lightly touching, thumbs and little fingers intertwining. The table trembles slightly, then tilts and very lightly taps on the carpet. Juliet opens her eyes wide, incredulous, like someone who has had too much good luck. She looks at the others questioningly. Valentina mumbles, her forehead in a frown:

VALENTINA: It's a new spirit. I can tell from the way it

moves the table. It's never manifested itself like this.

Juliet leans toward her and humbly, anxiously, like someone confessing a deep desire, says:

JULIET: Ask it something.

There is a silent pause.

VALENTINA: Can you tell us your name, spirit? (*The table beats out "I." Valentina successively calls out the letters, which Giorgio, in the armchair, writes down.*) I . . . R . . . I . . . S.
JULIET: Iris. What a beautiful name!
TABLE: I am beautiful.
VALENTINA: Have you a message for us, Iris?
TABLE: Love for all.
ALBA: Love for all? How lovely!
VALENTINA: Thank you, Iris. You're very sweet. Yours is a delightful message. Dear, would you like—

She stops herself because the table starts shaking violently. Juliet is very tense.

JULIET: What is it?
VALENTINA (*disconcerted*): I don't know. (*The table again shakes violently.*) Maybe it's an interference. Is that still you, Iris?

The table beats out a decisive "No."

CHIERICHETTA: It said no. Who can it be?
VALENTINA (*eyes closed, as if she alone were listening to voices from within, addressing herself softly to the table*): Are you at peace with God?

The table beats out a loud message, and above it all the hands sway rhythmically, all the participants counting and reciting as in a disciplined classroom.

ALL (*loudly*): O...F...C...O...U...R...

ALBA (*eagerly and greedily*): "Of course." It said, "Of course." It is at peace with God.

Juliet would like to suggest a question and leans over the table, her eyes shining. But Valentina dominates the situation. Authoritatively, but with false humility, she asks:

VALENTINA: Can you tell us your name?

The table taps its message like a precise telegram. Quickly raising her head, Juliet is the first to interpret the message. With a holy attitude, she spells out:

JULIET: O...L...A...F.

CHIERICHETTA (*fascinated, approving*): It's Olaf, yes.

ALBA (*mumbling to Valentina, who nods her head*): Turkish. Born in Turkey. (*She speaks to the table.*) You're Turkish, aren't you?

TABLE: Maybe *you're* Turkish.

There is a pause. Then, other beats.

CHIERICHETTA: He said, "*Troia*." *

VALENTINA (*sweetly, interpreting, asks*): Oh, Troy. Born in Troy, the ancient city.

TABLE: No!

ALBA: Have you a message for each one of us?

VALENTINA: Can you tell us something sweet, which might help us live, help us understand the meaning of our lives?

TABLE: Yes.

VALENTINA: Thank you, dear. What can you say to my friend Alba?

TABLE: *Troia.*

VALENTINA: No, dear, you didn't understand.

---

* The word *troia* has a double meaning in Italian: "whore" and "Troy."—Tr.

TABLE: Big whore!

The taps become louder as Valentina begins to trace the sign of the cross on the table.

VALENTINA: Go in peace. Go in peace, poor spirit. Go in peace.

Then suddenly the table taps out the name of Juliet. Alba, very excited, calls out:

ALBA: Juliet, a message for you.

Juliet turns pale.

TABLE: What are you up to? What's come into your head? Just what do you think you are? You're nothing; you don't count at all. You're of no importance to anyone . . . to anyone.

Juliet, now deathly pale, tries to say something. Doing her best to get up, she suddenly collapses, senseless.

ALBA: Juliet!
VALENTINA: Darling, darling. What are you doing? Stop. Don't break the chain.

Very excited, they all surround her, hold her up, call to her. With an almost sadistic compassion, Chierichetta exclaims:

CHIERICHETTA: She's going to die right here!
ALBA: A little water?

She hurriedly opens the door and goes into the next room. They all stand around Juliet, still unconscious. They call to her, try to make her drink, wet her face, slap her, but she doesn't come to.

VOICES: Juliet! Some cognac! Some water! Vinegar! Juliet!

GIORGIO: I know her. She shouldn't have . . . I said so. Juliet!

VALENTINA: Juliet! She isn't coming to. Call a doctor. What are you waiting for? My God!

ALBA (*looking around*): The telephone . . .

GIORGIO: No, no. Wait. All right. It's over. All right. Juliet? Up, up.

Juliet opens her eyes with difficulty. She looks around as they call to her, smile at her, make her smell vinegar and gulp down a little water. She slowly recovers consciousness.

She looks at the faces of those around her, in an effort to recognize them. Finally, as if overcome by a sudden terror, her eyes search for her husband. She sees him and stares at him desperately. Suddenly she throws her arms around his neck, pulling him tightly toward her, with a muffled sob.

JULIET'S HOME. EXTERIOR. DAYTIME.

The next day. The morning light—a very clear morning— falls on Juliet's house. All green, all bright, all serene. The chirping of birds.

JULIET'S BEDROOM. INTERIOR. DAYTIME.

The noise of an automobile leaving awakens Juliet. She looks around in the half-light of the room—the blinds are still closed—and sees that Giorgio is gone. She calls out.

JULIET: Fortunata!

FORTUNATA'S VOICE: Signora.

JULIET: Has my husband left already?

FORTUNATA'S VOICE: He just left. He said to tell you he didn't want to wake you because you were up late last night. (*She pauses.*) He said he won't be home for dinner.

Juliet stays in bed a few moments more, eyes staring into emptiness. She then gets up, goes to the window and opens

it. Sunshine and light invade the room. She remains in front
of the open window, attracted by the sweetness of the sun
and light. Almost inadvertently, she mutters:

JULIET: Love for all.

It is as if the shadow of the previous night had left her;
she breathes more freely, her features relax. She leaves the
window and goes to the bathroom while the window curtains swell with air and luminous reflections. She instinctively stops in front of the mirror for the usual examination
of her face. She calls out:

JULIET: Fortunata.
FORTUNATA'S VOICE: Signora.

Juliet goes to the living room. Everything is still in great
disorder. She looks around; her eyes stop at the three-legged
table.
She slowly goes to sit down in an armchair a few feet
from the table, continuing to stare at it. She gets up and approaches the table; she hesitates, then touches it.
Immediately the table jumps and moves. Juliet pulls her
hands back, and then, after some hesitation, she again places
them on the table. The table taps.

JULIET (*in a choked voice*): Who are you?
TABLE (*clearly*): I . . . R . . . I . . . S.

Juliet pulls her hands back, moves away, disturbed, glanc-
ing back at the table.

THE BEACH AT FREGENE. EXTERIOR. DAYTIME.

Juliet, in a beach outfit, is seated under an umbrella. With
her are a very fat and serious couple: Don Raffaele, the local
doctor, and his wife. All three are eating, helping themselves
from a portable table; above all, Don Raffaele and his wife
are eating. The beach is still almost deserted. A short dis-

tance from the group a child of three or four is seated in the sun, playing with sand and humming to herself.

DON RAFFAELE: What spirits, dear signora? What spirits? It's animal magnetism. A magnetic force that springs from our own being. Science is definite about this; there's no doubt any more. It's the bioelectric cell that comes into play. (*He stops a moment, busy enjoying some seafood.*) No, no. For heaven's sake, no lemon. Lemon changes the taste of seafood—which must be enjoyed as it truly is. (*He takes up the discussion again.*) The bioelectric cell acts on the common cultural base. To a certain degree, Freudian complexes, too, come into play. A chain of electromagnetic charges is created —my bioelectric cell with yours, with his. No water, thank you; wine. Dear signora, these experiences are absolutely inadvisable; they have a negative effect on the nervous system.

JULIET: Sometimes, when I was a child, all I had to do was close my eyes and I saw—

DON RAFFAELE: I see when I open my eyes, dear signora.

JULIET: No, I mean . . . I used to see . . . people I didn't know . . . places. Now, instead . . .

Juliet closes her eyes as if to illustrate what she means and immediately feels a tremor. For a brief moment she has seen a flash of beautiful womanly forces.

Iris, perhaps?

Juliet opens her eyes again; she is upset and remains lost in emptiness while the doctor continues to speak.

Only the child turns suddenly toward Juliet, smiling at her, letting out a happy trill, indicating the luminous air in front of her.

DON RAFFAELE: Such things are often digestive phenomena, dear signora. Digestion . . . the solar plexus slightly disturbed. Toxins, entering in a circle, reach the cerebral nervous centers. The hypophysis, in turn . . . a congestion forms.

Don Raffaele's discourse is interrupted by the sound of a helicopter, which passes right over the umbrella and lands on the beach nearby. Juliet and her friends watch it with curiosity.

From the cabin of the helicopter there emerges a beautiful half-dressed woman—Susy—who turns to wave goodbye to the pilot as the helicopter takes off.

Susy keeps waving toward the sky; then, slowly, sure of herself, paying no attention to her surroundings, she crosses the beach and goes into the pine forest.

Her passage has left breathless not only Juliet and her friends, but also the two or three young men scattered along the beach. It has been like an apparition of a superb feminine divinity.

> DON RAFFAELE (*recovering*): This, yes. This is an apparition I believe in.
> HIS WIFE (*chewing*): Last year I gave her massages. She has skin like silk. It disgusted me. (*She pauses, then speaks with hostility.*) She's the mistress of an industrialist. A man with white hair.
> JULIET: I know. Her house is near mine.

DISSOLVE

Later. Siesta time. Juliet is stretched out on the sand, half asleep. The doctor and his wife have moved away and are seated in the distance. The beach and sea are completely deserted.

Juliet closes her eyes, and, from the deserted sea, right in front of her, there emerges from a large bubble of gray water a large raft of wood and iron, loaded with ferocious and savage men. They carry weapons, barbaric armor, and daggers; they wear caps similiar to the Fascist fezzes, with skull and crossbones, and bear strange flags covered with monsters and dragons. Their faces are those of Mongols, with drooping moustaches and rough-shaven beards. Juliet quickly opens her eyes, looking at the sea. The raft is there, in front of her; it is slowly approaching the shore. On its side, in large letters, is written OLAF.

Beyond the first raft, others are seen, these, too, loaded with mysterious warriors and with savage, shaggy horses.

Juliet tries to get up, terrified, with an instinctive desire to flee. She is at first unable to get to her feet and for a few moments crawls forward. Then she begins to run, stumbling as she does. Panting, frightened, she turns around. The rafts are still there, and now some of the warriors, naked, are on the beach, pulling the rafts to shore with huge ropes.

Juliet starts to run again, arriving almost at the dunes. Short of breath, she stops again, looking over her shoulder.

But now the rafts are gone, taking with them the savage warriors and horses, leaving behind no trace. The sea stretches out, calm and luminous, disappearing from sight.

Juliet closes her eyes, then opens them again, passing her hands over her eyes and forehead. She looks around at the sea again. She is startled by the sound of a car horn.

A car has stopped in the little road near her. From it come two children, who greet her happily. They are her niece and nephew, children of her sister Adele, who is behind the wheel of the car. Next to Adele is Juliet's mother, an imposing woman, authoritative and cool, with a still-young face crowned by rich gray-and-blue hair. She is very elegant, as is Adele, who is beautiful, maternal, self-assured.

CHILDREN: Aunty. Hello, Aunty.

Juliet kisses them and goes to the car.

JULIET: Mamma, hello. Hello, Adele.
MOTHER: Where've you been? Whenever I come to see you, you're out. It's as if you did it on purpose. (*As Juliet leans over to kiss her, she pulls away.*) No, you're all wet.
JULIET: I was just going home. Let's go. Do you want some coffee?
MOTHER: It's too late now. (*She turns to Adele, speaking in a tone that implies the confidence of one friend speaking to another of things that concern only the*

two of them.) What time do we have to be at Luciana's?
ADELE: At four. And first we have to stop off so that I
can have my corset fitted.
MOTHER: Didn't Giorgio tell you? I called him myself.
ADELE: Where is your husband?
JULIET: In his office, working.
ADELE (*ironic, somewhat hostile*): He works so much!
It's impossible to see him ever. Never a Sunday, never
a vacation. Get in, children.
JULIET: What do you mean? In a month—he said he'll
take a real rest. Maybe we'll take a cruise. To Spain or
to Greece. We haven't decided yet, but I've got all the information. (*Her tone has suddenly become uncertain as
she realizes that her mother is staring at her.*) What's
wrong? Have I said something?
MOTHER: No, nothing. I was just looking. Don't you ever
put cream on? You really don't take care of yourself.
Give my best to Giorgio. So long. Call me tomorrow.

The car leaves.

JULIET'S HOME. INTERIOR. EVENING.

Juliet and Giorgio are on the sofa watching television,
which is about to end for the evening. Juliet is stretched
out next to her husband, holding his hand between hers.
She isn't watching the television; instead, she is listening to
sounds from the garden, as if not quite sure about her
hallucination. Giorgio yawns.

The television program ends. The music has ended, the
lightened square finally darkens. Giorgio yawns again.

GIORGIO: All right. Let's go to bed.
JULIET (*not wanting to go to bed*): Are you tired?
GIORGIO: Of course. All day—and tomorrow, too. Uff!

He frees himself from Juliet, leaving her seated on the
sofa like a puppet, and goes to turn off the set. He also
turns off a lamp. Juliet fixes her hair. She would like to tell
her husband about the invaders. She begins.

JULIET: Today . . .

GIORGIO (*turning around, obviously not interested and rather bored*): Today?

JULIET (*sighing and deciding not to tell the story because it wouldn't be believed*): Nothing. I went to the beach today; it was beautiful.

GIORGIO (*hypocritically*): I envy you. I . . . the sea . . .

He starts to go toward the bedroom.

JULIET: Would you take a look in the garden, to see if everything's in order?

GIORGIO (*looking at her, surprised, but, too tired to object, heading for the garden*): Why?

JULIET: Just to be sure. And close the blinds tightly.

GIORGIO (*turning off the garden lights*): Always full of cats. More every day.

He yawns again and loosens his tie with a tired gesture.

SHORTLY AFTERWARDS, IN BED

Juliet, still wide-awake, is getting into bed. Her husband is already under the covers, head buried in the pillow, eyes closed.

Juliet takes a large colored handkerchief and puts it over the small lampshade on the night table, to reduce the light. She takes a book from the night table, opens it and tries to immerse herself in it. The miaowing of cats is heard from the outside.

Silence. Then Giorgio mumbles confusedly:

GIORGIO: Ga . . . briella.

JULIET (*turning toward her husband, softly*): What did you say?

GIORGIO (*sleepily, as if answering a painful question*): Ga . . . briella. (*Juliet puts the book down and watches her husband as he mutters other incomprehensible words.*) Assa . . . tuti . . . colo.

Juliet feels a sudden chill. She remains immobile, eyes wide open as she watches her husband. Then she decides. Softly, sweetly, she tries to continue the questioning.

JULIET: Who is—who is Gabriella?
GIORGIO (*at first silent, then again mumbling in his sleep*): Amonomonio.

After this meaningless word, he begins to snore quietly, then makes a sound as if his throat were being cut, quiets down, and again snores lightly, calmly.

JULIET (*sweet, inviting*): Come on. Who is Gabriella?

Giorgio answers with a grunt, turns over on his side, and goes into a deep sleep. Juliet stays still, watching him, hoping that he might again talk in his sleep. Finally she gives up. It is clear that he won't talk again, at least for the moment. She puts her head down on the pillow and looks up at the shadows that the lamp casts on the ceiling and on the walls. Troubling shadows. She closes her eyes, muttering to herself.

JULIET: Who is Gabriella? Who is she?

THE FOLLOWING MORNING.

Giorgio, dressed and ready to leave, hat on his head, though raised on his forehead, is finishing his hurried breakfast. He quickly butters a piece of bread and looks for the honey. Juliet puts it in front of him. With full mouth, he mutters a thank-you. Juliet, in her bathrobe, is seated across from him. She reaches out to take a cigarette from his pack. This gesture is enough to make her husband show his bad humor.

GIORGIO: You're starting already. Can't you stop it? (*Juliet shrugs her shoulders, lighting the cigarette. She inhales the smoke with an exaggerated smile. Her husband finishes up his coffee and then speaks, as if suddenly reminded of something.*) Oh, I won't be home to

eat. I have too much to do. I'll have a sandwich somewhere.

Juliet doesn't move. She puts the newly lit cigarette out
in the coffee cup. Her husband looks at her, a bit surprised;
he says nothing. He gets up to leave, giving his wife the
usual kiss. Juliet accepts the kiss without returning it, staring blankly.

GIORGIO: Good-bye.

He goes toward the door to the veranda.

JULIET (*quietly, not moving*): Who is Gabriella?

Giorgio stops as if someone had pointed a gun at him.
For a brief moment he doesn't dare turn around. Then,
afraid that Juliet might notice that he is disturbed, he turns
around with a serious and questioning face.

GIORGIO: Gabriella? (*Then he speaks as if he had heard
the name for the first time.*) Why? What has that got
to do with anything?
JULIET (*forcing a smile, repeating simply*): Gabriella.
GIORGIO (*pulling himself together*): Are you joking?
JULIET: No, because . . . last night, in your sleep, you
said "Gabriella" twice.
GIORGIO (*encouraged, since he feared the worst*): That?
Who knows? Maybe I was dreaming.
JULIET (*very calmly*): You were probably dreaming of
Gabriella. Who is she? Do I know her?
GIORGIO (*now sure of himself*): But even I don't know
your Gabriella! (*He bursts into laughter, a little forced,
and shakes his head, pretending to be amused.*) So
many things are said in dreams. I don't know any
Gabriella. You misunderstood. So long. If I finish up,
I might come back—or I'll call. Good-bye, dear.

He goes out. Juliet is tense, continues to look at him as he

crosses the garden. He opens the gate and disappears.
Juliet doesn't move.

THE GARDEN OF JULIET'S HOME. EXTERIOR. DAYTIME.

Juliet, seated in a deck chair, is peeling apples, which she
then puts into a saucepan. Around her everything sparkles
with dew or a recent rain. There are small rainbows everywhere. The usual cats are either drowsing or slipping silently
through the grass and the bushes. Juliet is pensive. Peeling
an apple, she keeps a large ribbon of the peeling in her hand;
she lets it wave in the air, puts it into different shapes and
makes it dance in a dewy ray of sun. Meanwhile, she murmurs to herself.

JULIET: Gabriella?

She lets the skin fall into a basket and gets ready to work
on another apple. Valentina approaches from the back of the
garden. She wears a long fur that goes down to her feet;
on her head is a knitted, three-cornered beret.

VALENTINA (*from the distance*): How marvelous! How
marvelous, dear! Look, the dew! It's so beautiful that it
pains me.

She stops in the middle of the path, wetting her hands
and forehead in the foliage.

JULIET: It's rain.
VALENTINA: What purity . . . the rain . . . the dew!
(*She makes a cup with her hands and drinks from it.*)
I'd like to roll in it, naked. Why can't we do things
like that? Why? Tell me. See how complicated and un-
civilized we are. (*She kisses and embraces Juliet.*) Darling, what are you doing?

She sits on the arm of Juliet's chair, takes an apple and
bites into it.

JULIET: Baked apples.

VALENTINA: See what a little housewife you are! I am the negation of one. I'm ashamed of myself. Tell me, why am I made this way? I feel so rootless, so at loose ends. Take baked apples as an example. If I could make them, maybe I'd be saved.

Juliet gets up, takes the saucepan and goes toward the house. Valentina follows her.

JULIET: I'm going to light the oven. I'm coming right back. It's almost noon.

VALENTINA: Don't tell me it's noon already. It's not possible. I have a date with Roberto in the Piazza di Spagna at eleven. What an idiot I am. Darling, I've got to run. I'm going. My God, it's wet here. Don't you suffer from the dampness? I couldn't stand it. Darling, see you tonight. At ten.

She kisses Juliet and then rushes toward the gate.

JULIET: Are you coming back tonight?

VALENTINA (*stopping suddenly*): Oh, I didn't tell you.

JULIET: What?

VALENTINA: Didn't I tell you? That's just why I stopped by. Bhisma. Bhisma is at the Hotel Plaza tonight. You absolutely must come. He's wonderful, wonderful. You know, I told you about him. He arrived two days ago; I've already been to see him. He has two eyes—he has tremendous magic powers. You can speak to him; he can see through everything. You will be enlightened. He's an initiate, a seer.

LOBBY. HOTEL PLAZA. INTERIOR. NIGHT.

Coming in from the brightly lit and crowded street, Juliet and Valentina enter the total darkness of the hotel lobby. The only lights, from the stairways and the back of the lobby, come from flashlights.

VALENTINA (*crying out*): Oh, God!
JULIET: But it's completely dark.

A male voice comes from out of the darkness. It is the elevator boy.

ELEVATOR BOY: The electricity is gone, but it'll come back.
VALENTINA: But I can't see a thing. Where's the elevator?
ELEVATOR BOY: Over there. But it isn't working.

From the darkness, the loud, shrill voice of Alba, who then appears next to her two friends. She takes Juliet's arm.

ALBA: Valentina!
JULIET: Who is it? Alba?
ALBA: I was going to leave. If you hadn't arrived, I would have left. Who wants to climb the stairs in the dark? Who knows how many sadists there are in these rooms?
JULIET: What floor is he on?
VALENTINA (*complaining*): The fifth.
ALBA: What should we do? Leave?
JULIET: I want to go. Let's go. (*She turns to the elevator boy.*) Where are the stairs?
ELEVATOR BOY (*preceding them, flashlight in hand*): This way.

The three friends head for the stairs. The elevator boy leaves them.

VALENTINA: Oh, God, I can't see a thing. Where are you?
JULIET: Give me your hand. Wait . . . I have a lighter.

She lights the lighter, but Alba suddenly lets out a shriek of terror: A whitish form has suddenly appeared in the uncertain light of the flame, coming down from the stairway. It is a guest of the hotel, an elderly English lady, dressed in white, who passes before them as a ghost, a most dignified one.

ENGLISH LADY (*in English*): Oh, I apologize.

She disappears down the stairway.

ALBA: Wait. I'm going back—I can't make it. Five
flights—(*At that moment the lights come on again all
over the hotel. The three friends let out a cry of relief.
They are on the second floor, the elevator right in front
of them. Juliet hurries to push the button, but Alba
has a moment of uncertainty.*) And if they go out
again? We'll be stuck in the elevator.
VALENTINA: Oh, God. How awful. Don't even talk about
it.
ALBA: I warn you—if something like that happens, I'll
go out of my mind.

The elevator stops at the floor. Juliet opens the doors,
pushing her friends in.

JULIET: Come on. Nothing more can happen. Get in.

ELEVATOR. HOTEL PLAZA. INTERIOR.

The automatic doors of the elevator are about to close
tight when, down below, in the lobby, an unknown man
raises his arms in a dramatic gesture of warning. The doors
close completely. The elevator boy pushes a button and
the elevator starts to go up. The mirrors reflect the anxious
faces of Juliet, Valentina, and Alba.

JULIET (*disturbed*): What did that man want?

Nobody answers. Valentina keeps her eyes shut as if in
prayer. Alba holds her breath. The elevator arrives at its
destination, and the doors open on a large room.

VALENTINA: Thank God.

But just as the three women run out of the elevator, the
lights go out again and there is total darkness.

JULIET'S VOICE: Valentina, where are you?

VALENTINA'S VOICE: Darling, I'm here. Give me your hand.

ALBA'S VOICE: Juliet, is that you? A match—light a match.

In the darkness, we hear the heavy breathing of the three women.

A clap of thunder. A frightened cry. Finally, silence.

Suddenly the lights come on again, and Juliet finds herself in a room separated from the rest of the corridor by screens. In the room is a small crowd, made up largely of middle-aged women.

A few steps away is Bhisma.

He is a man of about forty, with a large round face, blondish hair, bright and laughing eyes. He smiles at everyone, often ending a sentence or leaving one unfinished in the middle with a smile. He speaks in a singsong voice, perspires heavily, and is very good-natured.

At his shoulder sits a large, strong, good-looking woman, his assistant, who watches over him as if he were sick. She is dressed in a sari.

The session is over; Bhisma is taking leave of the participants.

> BHISMA: The squaring of the circle includes both sexes in a totality. The alchemists knew everything. The *fermentatio,* the *conjunctio spiritum,* the symbolic coitus of Gabrico with his sister Beya . . . (*He looks around, smiling, and repeats himself, in an understanding tone.*) Beya . . . Beya . . . (*Though not understanding, all present nod in agreement. While his assistant wipes his brow with a handkerchief, he continues in the same tone.*) The two children of King Tabritius . . . (*There are signs of general agreement.*) Dangerous. Very dangerous. A mortal danger. During coitus Gabrico disappears into the body of Beya; the light of Logos becomes absorbed by Pysis.

ASSISTANT (*leaning toward him, whispering*): Maestro, tea.

BHISMA (*nodding, rising slowly and continuing*): It is the descent of the conscious into the unconscious. *Visio Arislei.* Incestuous coitus is essential; the pairing of opposites. (*He stops speaking, moans a little, and, smiling at everyone, begins immediately to leave.*) Good night. Good night.

They all surround him, shaking the hand that he flabbily offers as he makes a half sign of benediction. Among the small crowd, an elderly lady near Valentina is saying in a low conspiratorial voice:

LADY: He was marvelous.
OTHER LADY: Impressive. A really impressive trance.
LADY: When the lights went out, he had just gone into it. Only his eyes could be seen in the darkness, I swear it.
VALENTINA (*complaining*): My God, we missed it!

Valentina continues to moan; she sees that Bhisma, followed by his assistant, is heading toward the corridor, and rushes off to follow him.

CORRIDOR. HOTEL PLAZA. INTERIOR. NIGHT.

Valentina reaches Bhisma; Juliet and Alba stay a few feet behind.

VALENTINA: Maestro, Maestro, good evening. (*She points to Juliet and Alba, introducing them.*) My friends . . . Juliet . . . Alba. (*She continues hurriedly, pointing to Juliet.*) She wanted so badly to talk to you. She needs you, Maestro. To be led, enlightened.

Bhisma, instead of looking at Juliet, watches Alba, who is certainly much flashier, but he takes the hand of each woman, smiling sweetly. Over his shoulder his assistant makes mute signs of disapproval, which mean that the women should leave him in peace.

BHISMA: Yes, dear. Yes, dear. Alba? Alba?

He begins walking along the corridor; the three women don't know what to do. Juliet, unnerved, turns to Valentina and says in a low voice:

JULIET: Let's go. It's late. Let's leave.

But Valentina pushes her forward, while Alba, very excited, insists in a low voice:

ALBA: No ... No ...

In the meantime, Bhisma turns around and calls to them:

BHISMA: Come along, dear ones. Come along.

The assistant opens the door to a room. Bhisma enters, followed by the three women and the assistant.

BHISMA'S ROOM. INTERIOR. NIGHT.

Juliet, Valentina, and Alba are uncertain and ill at ease; they look around the room in silence. It is disordered; all the lamps are on; the bed is unmade. There are many books all around.

Bhisma, as if alone, moves calmly through the room. He takes a book, leafs through it and reads a little. He goes into the bathroom to wash his hands and face.

In a low, calm voice he exchanges a few sentences with his assistant, who closes the door and immediately starts busying herself. She takes a teacup, cleans it out, and puts sugar in it, then takes a thermos and pours some tea from it into the cup. Finally she adds a little brandy from a large bottle.

In the meantime, Bhisma goes to and from the bathroom, drying his hands and face.

BHISMA (*smiling*): Always in disorder, always in disorder. We are gypsies, gypsies. (*Smiling still, he shows the book he's been leafing through to the women.*) *The Kings.* Sit down, dear ones. (*He speaks to the assistant.*) Tea is beneficent. The drink of the ancient wise men of the East.

He goes into the bathroom; the running of the faucet is heard. The three women, seated, wait uncertainly. The assistant says to them, sweetly, in a whisper:

ASSISTANT: He's very tired. He was in a long and tiring trance.

As the assistant moves away, Alba, all tense, mutters to her friends:

ALBA: Do you feel it?
VALENTINA: What?
ALBA: There's a tremendously erotic atmosphere here. I suddenly want to take my clothes off and dance. (*More softly, excited, pointing to the bed, she goes on.*) They're lovers. Of course. I feel chills.

Valentina nods her head in agreement. Alba is about to say something, but Bhisma again appears from the bathroom, drying his hands. He begins to pace up and down the room slowly and aimlessly. The assistant follows him, taking the towel from him, and offers him the cup of tea. She says to him in a low voice:

ASSISTANT: Maestro . . . I put some brandy in it.

Bhisma smiles vaguely and, standing, drinks his tea. He is directly in front of Juliet and stares at her in silence. Juliet, unsettled by his look, doesn't know what to do and ends up by rising slowly to her feet.

BHISMA (*to the assistant*): Yes, dear, yes.

Valentina, grabbing the opportunity, says:

VALENTINA: Maestro, my friend really wanted to talk to you. You can really help her. (*She encourages Juliet.*) Tell him, tell him. Do you want us to leave you alone with him? Speak to him, darling.

Bhisma stops staring at Juliet and goes to sit in an armchair. In the meantime, the assistant goes back and forth from the bathroom, after having taken the cup from Bhisma. Juliet, making a great effort, says in a low voice:

JULIET: No, nothing . . . There was something . . . something that . . . (*She is silent a moment; then, getting back her courage, she almost whispers.*) Since last night it has seemed to me that I have nothing. I'm afraid I lack everything. I'm afraid my husband has another woman.

Bhisma, calm, continues to smile. The assistant pours a liquid on her hands and begins to massage his head. But now Bhisma is staring intently at Juliet.

BHISMA: Anxiety . . . yes . . . but you must enter into another dimension. Another dimension. All things are only in three; in the fourth they rejoice. (*A moment of silence, then he begins again, strangely calm.*) It's the fourth dimension. The *Lapis Philosophorum.* "Make of a man and a woman a circle. And from this extract a square, and from the square a triangle."

He closes his eyes as if from the massage and remains silent. Alba, still excited, takes his hand and examines it.

ALBA: May I, Maestro? I would so like to . . . I draw. I am a painter. I would like to make a sketch of you. Even of your hand alone. I can come tomorrow.

Bhisma doesn't answer; he puts his head back and closes his eyes completely. There is a long silence, and the three women look at each other, not knowing what to do. They watch the assistant, who is indicating to them that they should leave.

But suddenly Bhisma begins to act very oddly. Slow and increasingly effeminate movements from the arms and shoulders, accompanied by a stretching of—and a change in—the features of his face. An indefinable mark, almost too feminine, comes over his face. The assistant signals to the women not to move. Obviously the trance has begun. In a slow, soothing voice, the assistant asks:

ASSISTANT: Who are you, spirit?
BHISMA (*speaking in a strange voice, both sweet and sensual*): Iris.

Juliet starts; it is as if she perceived an extremely disturbing feminine presence around the shoulders of Bhisma. There is beauty and a sensuality of form and position. In the same voice, Bhisma begins again:

BHISMA-IRIS: Why don't you learn to please your husband, Juliet?

Juliet looks around. Upset, she answers in a hoarse voice, almost aggressively:

JULIET: I please my husband very much.

Bhisma breaks into laughter.

BHISMA-IRIS: I was born this way . . . a woman of love. Don't you find me beautiful? Speak freely.
JULIET (*after some hesitation, as if in a dream*): Yes. Very beautiful.
BHISMA-IRIS: Frankly, I, too, think I am beautiful. Yes, very beautiful. Have you seen my hair? I don't comb it; I caress it. I very much like to caress myself. I have such beautiful, fresh skin. When I'm in a bad mood, I go to the mirror and look at my back. I immediately become happy then. Have you bought stockings, Juliet?

JULIET: What stockings?

BHISMA-IRIS: Black net ones. All women want to be treated like fairies—and they don't know their job.

JULIET (*disturbed, aggressive*): Is love a job?

BHISMA-IRIS: I didn't say "job." I said "art." The art of loving. I had breasts when I was nine.

JULIET: No, I heard you very well. You said "job." A whore, then. Fine.

Once more a fresh and shameless laugh from the lips of Bhisma.

BHISMA-IRIS: Why don't you make yourself as beautiful as I am?

Bhisma's voice now fades out in a confused gurgle; the features of his face change again and another mask takes over, another voice comes from his lips. A masculine voice, persuasive and seductive, with a peculiar Spanish accent.

BHISMA: No one knows you, Juliet. No one sees you. Men no longer recognize real women. You are a real woman.

ASSISTANT: Who are you, spirit? Will you tell us your name?

BHISMA: I see all of you. Your breasts are beautiful, your hair is beautiful. Why are you afraid? You have extraordinary powers because your feminine sensuality is so refined. You are beautiful, Juliet. You are a real woman.

ASSISTANT: But who are you, who are you?

But Bhisma is coming to. He gurgles and stretches; his features return to normal.

THE COUNTRY. JULIET'S CAR. EXTERIOR. EVENING.

Juliet, deep in thought, drives along silently.
Valentina and Alba are sitting in the back of the car,

chattering in low voices, commenting on what they saw and heard at Bhisma's. The shadows of evening fall on the countryside, and the lights from the car briefly illuminate fantastic shapes of trees and houses.

> JULIET (*to herself*): Maybe Iris is the ballerina who ran away with my grandfather.
> VALENTINA: What, dear?
> JULIET: My grandfather was a schoolteacher. He fell in love with a beautiful ballerina. He was expelled from all schools because of this. I always imagined that my grandfather ran away in a balloon.

While Juliet speaks we see an immense field with fantastic shapes of early airplanes. At the center is a fabulous balloon, decorated with flags and shining with colored lanterns.

Juliet's grandfather comes running, leading a beautiful ballerina by the hand. He takes her by the arm, puts her in the enormous basket, and jumps in himself. The balloon, shimmering toward the sky, takes off. Down on the field, jumping up and down in anger, are Juliet's mother, her sisters, her father (in a Fascist uniform) and the principal of the school.

> JULIET: Down below were my mother, my father, and the principal of the school, all jumping up and down with rage. There was also Il Duce.
> VALENTINA: Why Il Duce, dear?
> JULIET: My father always said that Il Duce was the father of us all, so when I was a child I was very confused between my father and Il Duce. My father was a fanatic Fascist. My only memory of him is like that— in a black shirt, with high boots. He used to make us do gymnastics with the windows open, even in winter.

Juliet and her little sisters are seen, going through the rhythmic motions of gymnastics. They are clumsy and cold before a wide-open window; outside, all is frozen. The father, in a black shirt and high boots, leads them.

JULIET: I don't remember anything else about him, except for his funeral. My mother had a beautiful dress.

A hearse approaches the tomb, between two flanks of uniformed Fascists, daggers ready. A stentorian voice calls out:

VOICE: Comrade Boldrin!
FASCISTS: Present!

The mother, dressed in mourning, stands immobile, like a statue.

ALBA: What a stupendous woman your mother is, Juliet! Why don't you ask her if she'd come to pose?
JULIET: Yes, she is very beautiful. One night I got out of bed and went into the corridor. I saw her—she was just like a queen. Maybe she was going to a ball with my father. (*Juliet's mother, in a truly regal evening dress, shining with jewelry, appears at the end of the corridor. She turns slowly to Juliet and orders her to go back to bed.*) I used to watch for hours as the dressmakers fitted her clothes.

Juliet, deeply absorbed and saddened, continues to look ahead silently.

JULIET'S GARDEN. EXTERIOR. EVENING.

Juliet has arrived home.
She puts the key in the gate and opens it. She pushes a button and lights the garden lamp. In the middle of the flowering tree stands a man—tall, elegant, extremely handsome, with an air of nobility and vaguely melancholy. He is looking at a rose bush with detachment, but also with a certain very sad grace.
Juliet stands still.
The gentleman looks toward her with a smile and a slight move of the head, which, with extraordinary ease, replace a formal introduction.

GENTLEMAN: A gilded rose. A name almost as beautiful as a line of poetry. I used to grow them once, too. I had a garden full of them known by everyone in Spain. (*His voice strangely resembles that which Juliet heard in the session with Bhisma. Afraid of making a mistake, uncertain whether this man is an apparition or a real presence, Juliet looks around her as if for help. The handsome man gently caresses the long, bent stem and goes on, with a short bow.*) You are very lucky. Flowers are grateful to those who take care of them. They know how to show their gratitude. (*He approaches Juliet as if now were the moment to greet her formally, and, without a move on Juliet's part, he bows down to take her hand and kisses it with an exquisite gesture.*) These plants receive much love. In order to give them so much of it each day, it is obvious that you must be filled with love.

He walks away from her and, as if alone, goes quietly to the gravel path, where he caresses a bush of gladioli as if to test—as an expert—the thickness of their soft stems.

He reaches the front of the house, which casts a light into the garden. He stops and turns toward Juliet, waiting quietly, immobile as a statue, as if he did not feel the need to talk or as if this were his usual position.

At that moment, Fortunata comes out of the kitchen, bringing a carafe of water and a tray on which are pieces of orange and slices of lemon.

Looking at the gentleman—as at a very real presence—Fortunata comes toward him and shows him the tray.

FORTUNATA (*somewhat argumentatively*): All right? Everything you asked for? Nothing missing?

She then looks at Juliet as if to say, "He wanted it this way." She remains, watching with ironic diffidence.

With almost ritualistic gestures, the gentleman is pouring other liquids into the water and putting in the pieces of lemon and orange, mixing all together as if preparing a mysterious love potion. He smiles gently, coming to the end of the operation as he moves the silver spoon with the grace of a priest handling a chalice. He raises the carafe to the light, contemplates its magic iridescence, and then delicately pours a small quantity into the glass. However, he is immediately angered, puts the glass aside and, with mild contempt, says to Fortunata:

GENTLEMAN: Not these goblets; they're good for champagne. I need ordinary glasses.

Bending down to the little wood and straw table that serves as a garden bar, Juliet picks up a long, colored glass and says rapidly, zealously:

JULIET: Is this one all right?

The man watches her; he smiles, nods his head, and pours the liquid directly into the glass that Juliet is holding.

GENTLEMAN (*with elegance*): Taste it; tell me if it's right.

Tasting it with pleasure as if sipping a marvelous potion, Juliet swallows.

JULIET: It's delicious. (*Then, with candor*) What is it? What's it called?

The man smiles and, as if revealing an intimate secret, leans toward Juliet, saying:

GENTLEMAN: Shangri-la. Haven't you ever tasted it? They say that it takes away all thirsts from those who drink it, even that thirst which is never acknowledged. Maybe this one is the drink of forgetfulness. (*Juliet, without reason, blushes and stands silently with the glass in her hand. Leaning toward her, the man speaks in his usual tender and melancholy tone, full of remote implications.*) More. I'll pour you some more.

He doesn't wait for her answer; instead, he pours more of the drink into her glass. This gesture, the sound of the liquid filling the glass—their very positions—are almost excessively intimate; they seem indiscreet.

At that moment, Giorgio comes down the stairway.

> GIORGIO: I fixed your bed. You have to stay at least a week. Oh! Juliet! You've already met each other. You remember, Juliet, I spoke to you about José. I was his guest in Spain. He has a palace in Castile with twenty towers; inside are six paintings by Goya. What were they? Goya or Velásquez?
>
> JOSE: Neither one. Ribera.

Giorgio has gone to Juliet and distractedly kissed her on the cheek.

> GIORGIO: He wanted to stay in a hotel. (*To José.*) There is such silence, such peace here. I sleep all night and have beautiful dreams. (*Juliet looks at her husband with disapproval and distrust, as if she realized he is assuming attitudes that are not his. Giorgio notes the look and speaks to her, courageously.*) Did I ever tell you about my dreams?
>
> JULIET (*somewhat rudely*): No. Even when you talk in your dreams, you don't tell me about them afterward.

DISSOLVE

LIVING ROOM. JULIET'S HOME. INTERIOR. NIGHT.

The supper is finished. Juliet is seated at the table with Giorgio and José. The moonlight, which whitens the pines, enters the room. There is a long, almost rapturous silence. José begins to declaim, in a low voice, with sincere intensity:

> JOSÉ: *Nadie comprendia el profumo de la oscura magnolia de tu vientre. Nadie sabía que martirizabas un colibrí de amor entre los dientes.*

JULIET (*enchanted, speaking in the ingenuous tone of one inspired*): What is that? Garcia Lorca?

JOSÉ (*shocked*): You know "my" poet?

JULIET: They read him on television.

JOSÉ (*rapturously looking at Juliet, translates*): "No one understood the perfume of the dark magnolia of the womb . . ."

JULIET (*ill at ease*): Beautiful.

JOSÉ: "No one knew that you tormented a humming-bird—" that's a little bird—"a hummingbird of love between your teeth." Oh, it's beautiful. You must like poetry very much, I imagine.

Giorgio gets up and picks up a pair of binoculars.

GIORGIO: Look what a beautiful gift José brought me.

He goes into the garden.
Silence.
José looks at Juliet and then says:

JOSÉ: A strange feeling, this evening. Imagine, yesterday I was in Madrid. I didn't want to leave. Curious presentiments. And instead I'm now happy to be here. Very. What's left in the world if you take away friendship, new encounters, the harmony of an hour like this one? I am indebted to you for a moment of real happiness. And I hope it continues.

JULIET(*uncertain, ill at ease*): For so little.

JOSÉ (pensive): Little is everything sometimes. A sudden decision, a friend who lives by the sea—and a lost calm is rediscovered. All becomes clear, plausible.

Juliet gets up; she is disturbed. She goes to the veranda door. José follows and stops next to her.

JOSÉ (*reciting*): "*Magica luna, tanto sei consunta.*"

Juliet suddenly moves closer to her husband, who is looking at the moon through the binoculars.

GIORGIO: José, come here—come and look. (*He points to a lighted window in the villa next door. The disturbing figure of a woman is outlined against the curtains: It is Susy. She is naked.*) It's the girl friend of the Greek armament maker—that means millions.

José remains cold, detached. Juliet takes the binoculars and looks. The shape of the naked woman appears in the binoculars, with a magical effect: her breasts, her thighs, her back. Juliet is overwhelmed.

JULIET: What a beautiful woman!

She passes the binoculars to José, who doesn't even look through them; he gives them back to Giorgio. Susy is still seen through the lighted window.

JULIET'S BEDROOM. INTERIOR. EVENING.

Juliet and Giorgio are in bed. Giorgio, without getting up, is groping on the night table for his ear plugs; finding them, he carefully puts them in his ears to ensure tranquil sleep.
Juliet looks at him, somewhat disappointed, and says:

JULIET: The ear plugs already? Don't you want to talk even for a minute?
GIORGIO (*already deaf, vaguely annoyed*): What? I can't hear a thing.

He makes a polite, but obviously unwilling, gesture to take out the plugs. Juliet, a little bitterly, stops him.

JULIET: It doesn't matter.

Above, on the ceiling, the slow regular steps of a man are heard as he walks softly through the room in peaceful meditation. He stops and starts at regular intervals.
Juliet raises her face toward the ceiling and looks puzzled. Lights coming in from the window are reflected on the

ceiling. The pacing above begins again and then stops. The
blinds are being raised above, and now the man must have
stopped in front of the window to look out into the night.

THE HOUSE. EXTERIOR. NIGHT.

José, in an elegant robe, is leaning on the window sill,
silently smoking, immobile. His glance is lost among the
moonlit pines.

JULIET'S BEDROOM. INTERIOR. NIGHT.

Juliet, feeling alive in the presence of a man, instinctively
moves closer to her husband. She practically curls up on his
chest, a chest rising with the calm, innocent breath of sleep.
She sighs and closes her eyes. Above, the pacing begins again,
slow, almost unreal, but as regular as the rhythm of a beautiful verse.

Juliet smiles happily, though there is a vaguely frightened
expression on her face. She, too, begins to breathe in her sleep
as if lulled by the steps above.

JULIET'S BEDROOM. INTERIOR. NIGHT.

The room is dark as Juliet sleeps. She is suddenly awakened by something. An indistinct voice is heard from the
kitchen, and a small light shows through the bottom of the
closed door.

Juliet instinctively turns toward Giorgio, next to her. But
he is gone. Overcome by irrational anxiety, Juliet gets out of
bed and, barefoot, goes rapidly to the door and opens it.

JULIET'S LIVING ROOM. INTERIOR. NIGHT.

Having opened the door, Juliet abruptly finds herself in
front of her husband, who is speaking on the telephone in a
muffled voice. Giorgio, upon seeing her, immediately hangs
up the receiver. For a few moments, they are silent, looking
at each other, pale.

Then Giorgio says, with effort:

GIORGIO: I forgot to put a call in . . . to be awakened at seven.

Passing in front of Juliet without even looking at her, he goes into the bedroom, taking refuge in his bed.

Juliet remains motionless. The voice that comes forth is faint and weary.

JULIET: Who were you calling?
GIORGIO (*from the bed, awkwardly*): What? The wake-up service—I told you.

He closes his eyes, covering his face with the sheet.

DISSOLVE

A STREET IN ROME. EXTERIOR. DAYTIME.

A street crowded with cars passing quickly in all directions. Suddenly the sound of a loud whistle. The cars stop abruptly, some at once, some with small delay, while the whistle continues to be heard. Among the cars is Juliet's. She is seated behind the wheel next to her sister, Adele. Juliet, like the other drivers, looks around, surprised and concerned.

A very small hunchback is crossing the street, weaving through the rows of stopped cars, continuing to blow on his whistle in order to get ahead.

He reaches the sidewalk and disappears among the crowd. The drivers, incredulous, have watched him pass. Now traffic continues.

Juliet continues to drive but, amused, keeps looking around for the hunchback. Adele, however, looks across the street, at a store window. She is calm and uninterested.

ADELE: You must remind me . . . on this corner . . . just the little shoes I was looking for for Gigi. Can't you stop here? Just for a minute. As it is, we're very near already.

Juliet finds an empty space and parks the car. The two
sisters get out together, and Adele goes back a few steps
to the store window, to look at the shoes more carefully.
Juliet waits for her; she is preoccupied, disturbed, restless.
She realizes that Adele has rejoined her and is speaking to
her; she follows her without listening.

ADELE: I can't tell you how many shoes she wears out.
She eats them up. Not Lorella, on the other hand.
Nothing. A pair of shoes like this . . .

Juliet has been following her own thoughts. She says suddenly, agitated but resolved:

JULIET: Yes, yes. Absolutely. Better to do this than go
on doubting. Enough. I can't stand it. What do you
think? Don't you agree?
ADELE (*calmly and disdainfully*): You should have done
it sooner. But you're always the same.
JULIET: You're right. It's a kind of liberation. There's
always the chance that they might just be crazy ideas
of my own, ones I dreamed up. Maybe. In fact, why
not?
ADELE (*in the same tone*): No.
JULIET: No? Why not? It's probable. I don't have any
proof at all. Only these vague suspicions. I might be
ruining my life for no reason, don't you think?
ADELE: No, no.
JULIET: No?
ADELE: No. But at least you can get the taste of putting
his back to the wall. The liar! You show him what a
liar he is! The satisfaction of seeing him turn white—
white as this! Proof in hand. I want to be there, too.
Call me.
JULIET. Yes.
ADELE: Give me a ring as soon as you have the proof,
and I'll come right away. We'll wait for him together.
If you don't have the courage to talk to him, fool that
you are, I'll do it.

She stops to look at another shop window. Juliet, her eyes full of tears, stops and waits for her. Then her eyes are attracted to a large colored balloon that has escaped from someone and is climbing up over the roofs.

She follows the balloon with her eyes. Adele calls to her. Choking up, her voice changed, Juliet mutters:

JULIET: I can't go on. . . .

She realizes that Adele is leading her toward a door. She stops.

ADELE: Isn't this it? Here it is.

She reads the sign: OCCHIO DI LINCE (Eyes of a Lynx).

JULIET: Oh, yes.

Adele enters, sure that Juliet will follow her, but Juliet remains on the sidewalk. After a moment, Adele reappears at the entrance. Juliet, choked up, says:

JULIET: You go.
ADELE: And you? Why?

Without answering, Juliet walks away. Adele hurries after her, reaches her and takes her arm.

JULIET: It's only cowardice. I can't. First name, last name, address. They spy on him, follow him. He'll even want photographs. He might, you'll see.
ADELE: Of course he'll want photographs. Are you crazy?
JULIET: I can't. Let it be. I don't feel like it. Basically, he is my husband. I'm a coward. Let's go away from here.

Adele, always calm, is nevertheless angry. She particularly dislikes such a scene in the middle of the street. She glances about nervously, turning with Juliet toward the entrance.

ADELE: Crazy fool. What are you doing, idiot?

JULIET: Basically, he is my husband. My husband—not yours.

ADELE: In front of all these people, in the middle of the street. Crazy! Everyone's watching us. You made the appointment. Fool!

Juliet has stopped listening. She is staring at something or someone in the crowd, and, looking behind her, she passively lets herself be pushed into the doorway.

Among the crowd, for an instant, she has seen what seems to be a bearded monk, with a thin face and bare feet. He has stared at her with flaming eyes, pointing out, imperatively and threateningly, the entrance to the agency.

OFFICE OF THE AGENCY. INTERIOR. DAYTIME.

Juliet and Adele are seated in front of a desk. On the other side is the large head of Occhio di Lince, covered with a Basque cap. He has a pointed beard and is short and thickset, wider than he is long. He looks like a large gnome. His pipe is on the table. He is taking notes.

OCCHIO DI LINCE: Where does the subject live? (*No one answers.*) The address?

ADELE: Via delle Mimose, eight.

JULIET: Seven.

ADELE: I always thought it was eight.

OCCHIO DI LINCE: Has he an office? (*The two women nod.*) Where? Office address.

Adele looks at Juliet, who, in a halting voice, as if to gain time, says:

JULIET: There's also an associate in the office.

OCCHIO DI LINCE: So?

ADELE: What does that matter?

JULIET: Of course it doesn't matter.

ADELE: He's in via . . . What street? Isn't he in via Ponchielli?

JULIET: Twenty-five.

OCCHIO DI LINCE: What kind of office? What type of work does our man do?

Juliet shrugs her shoulders, making vague gestures. Adele breaks in again.

ADELE: He receives people. I don't know. Organizes parties, doesn't he? What does he do? I never really understood.

OCCHIO DI LINCE: Public relations man—something like that? (*Juliet nods a yes. Very proud of having deduced this, he continues.*) What kind of hours does he keep? What time does he leave home; what time does he return? At what time is he in his office?

ADELE: Return? He hardly ever returns.

JULIET: Of course he does. What do you mean, he doesn't? In the evening; a little late.

ADELE: And in the morning, what time does he leave? Eight? Eight-thirty?

JULIET: Nine.

Without raising his eyes, Occhio di Lince reaches out his hand.

OCCHIO DI LINCE: A picture, please.

Juliet takes the pictures out of her pocketbook, hands trembling, and says almost angrily to her sister:

JULIET: You see?

ADELE: Of course.

Occhio di Lince examines the two pictures, comparing them; he lights his pipe. He will now give a sample of his astuteness and psychological perception.

OCCHIO DI LINCE: Thirty-five . . . thirty-seven. A man of stature. Authoritarian in a certain sense. (*He looks inquiringly at the two women and then answers him-*

self.) Quick-tempered? Yes, that, too . . . success with women . . . not a simple character. The forehead, here —the lines of the forehead. Capable of hurried decisions, not always thought out. Watch out. This . . . yes. But not really bad. (*More and more smoke emerges from the pipe, and this smoke makes the face of Occhio di Lince seem increasingly unreal to Juliet.*) What time can we call you—without embarrassing anyone? Morning? Yes, morning. Within a week or ten days. Yes, that's enough time. We have the most modern methods. Miraculous. Very reliable men. You can relax. The basic cost is thirty thousand lire. Tape recorder. Marvelous. Telecameras. Telephoto lens.

The smoke becomes thicker and thicker; the large head of the gnome almost disappears in it, the voice fading away.

THE STREET TO JULIET'S HOME. EXTERIOR. DAYTIME.

Juliet is slowly walking toward the gate of her home. She is preoccupied, obviously upset by the decision she has been forced to make. She arrives at the gate and through the bars she sees the Spaniard; he is swinging on the garden swing.

Juliet has no desire to speak, so she withdraws, unobserved. She looks around hesitantly and goes into the next street. She now walks more slowly—to pass time—but at the end of the street she sees Don Raffaele's wife approaching. Not wanting to meet her, either, she turns off into a silent little path that leads to the pine forest.

She is walking through the pines when suddenly the sound of galloping startles her. Across the pines she sees a shaggy, savage horse advancing, belly to the ground. On the horse sits—without saddle or stirrup—a barbarous warrior, with the face of a Mongol.

The rider comes to within a few steps of Juliet, stops the horse roughly, and, for a few moments, stares at her with glassy eyes, in silence.

The horse stamps the ground with his hoof, and his hot breath reaches Juliet's face. Then the warrior kicks the horse and departs at a slow gallop, heading in the direction from which he came.

Juliet, terrified, follows him with her eyes. Among the pines, in the distance, she sees three more barbarous warriors standing around a fire that surrounds a tree stump on which a skinned ram is being roasted. The three warriors, standing still, are looking in Juliet's direction.

The booming sound of a jet in take-off comes from the sky—right above Juliet. An unbearable roar.

Then the voice of a woman calling Juliet by name.

ALBA'S VOICE: Juliet!

Juliet, still upset, turns around. She sees a shed overlooking the sea; at a large glass window is Alba, gesturing to her.

ALBA'S STUDIO. INTERIOR. DAYTIME.

Alba is at the door, dressed in work clothes, with brush and palette, dirty with colors.

JULIET: What a strange dream! Was I dreaming?

She realizes that she has entered a large room, furnished as a studio. Everywhere there are paintings—finished and unfinished. They represent naked bodies of men and women with limbs in pagan positions, strange flowers—a little macabre and somewhat obscene—trees of disturbing, carnal shapes.

Alba is very excited, a little hysterical, about the work in which she is involved. Her laughter and shrill speech are even wilder than usual.

ALBA: Will you lend me your husband, Juliet? Just for a few days. (*She leads Juliet to the painting on which she is working and shows her a corner of the canvas, which is still empty but already contains sketches of powerful bodies of naked men.*) I'll put him here. Completely naked. There's no sense in representing God as some kind of abstraction, just a soul. God is much more; he is the greatest body there is.

Juliet is still shaken; only now does she realize that in the studio, in addition to Alba, there are two muscular and surly young men, who are posing; also present, in a short white tunic, is Chierichetta. Juliet looks anxiously toward the beach, now completely deserted, while Alba continues ahead—moving through the studio, drinking, coming back to one of her models or suddenly caressing Juliet.

ALBA: God as a body I can love and possess. A hero of perfect form—one I can desire and also take as a lover. We must give back to God his vital joy. Distribute physical joy in his name. (*A note of terror comes into her voice.*) At first I was afraid of God. He crushed me, terrified me. (*Again, as a reaction, she becomes explosive, carnal.*) No. Paradise is a field in which love is made. But eternally. You see? My paintings always represent the physical God, the corporeal God who populates the earth.

Juliet has not understood this discussion very well. She asks, still rather tense:

JULIET: A glass of water, please.

Chierichetta hurries to get the water for her. She drinks it with relish, while Alba puts her two models back into position and continues her work.

CHIERICHETTA: It's the neomystic school. The new physiological mysticism.
ALBA: "A body is a body is a body is a body." You know Gertrude Stein? "A rose is a rose is a rose is a rose." For me, instead, the secret of the world is: "A body is a body is a body is a body." Now sit over there quietly. Or do you want to pose, too? Get undressed!

Alba laughs harshly. Juliet is silently seated on a large, worn-out sofa. Now Alba, inspired, paints; everything is peaceful, silent.

Juliet looks at the models, then at the painting; then she slowly speaks:

> JULIET: When I was a child, I used to think that God was hidden behind the large dusty wooden shutters—always covered with cobwebs, always closed—in the nuns' little theater.

THE LITTLE THEATER OF THE NUNS. INTERIOR. NIGHT.

The large shutters are above the curtain, behind the lighted spotlights, which throw ribbons of light onto the stage below. There the children of the school are in the midst of the performance.

The voices of the children reciting are heard. The child-like voices reach to the top, to the closed, cobweb-covered shutters.

On the stage itself, the little girls, in Roman costume, are giving a sacred representation; they are dressed as warriors, lictors, magistrates, and Christian martyrs.

> JULIET'S VOICE: That year the nuns had us represent the life of a martyr, and I was chosen for the part of the martyr.

In the wings, while the play goes on, three smiling, busy nuns are finishing Juliet's makeup just before her turn comes to go on stage. They dress her in a little white tunic; around her head goes a halo of gilded paper.

The eldest nun has just finished putting gray cream on the face and brow of the child, who now looks very pale, cadaverlike. Next to this child is another, Laura, dressed as an angel. She, too, is obviously tense and anxious. While these operations proceed hurriedly, Juliet raises her eyes to look at the closed shutters.

The other child, too, looks up toward the shutters.

The youngest nun, watching Juliet's face transfixed by an

internal flame of certain and absolute faith, says to her sweetly:

YOUNG NUN: Juliet, what a smile you have today! You really seem to be the saint, the true one.

She takes out a magnifying glass and holds it over a little colored picture, comparing Juliet's face to the one in the picture. Juliet asks softly:

JULIET: But she—the saint—she saw God—later?
OLD NUN: When she flew to heaven, among the flames of martyrdom.
LAURA (*in a low voice*): Then you swear it? You'll tell me everything? Only me? (*Juliet promises.*) And you'll ask Him if He loves me?

Juliet, already ecstatic, raises her eyes toward the mysterious home of God when she is rudely seized by two larger companions, dressed as warriors, who pull her toward the stage. The nuns whisper to her, anxious and encouraging:

NUNS: It's your turn. Go—go. Courage.

On the stage a child dressed in a Roman toga, as a judge, her hair tied with laurel, comes solemnly forward and, reciting with strange conviction, obviously indicated in the text, says to Juliet:

GIRL-JUDGE: So, you have decided? You renounce your faith? You will make sacrifices to the emperor?

Raising her head with a very lively movement, pale with enthusiasm, Juliet clearly pronounces, joyfully:

JULIET: No, never.

The girl continues to insist, emphatically, but with sincere anger:

GIRL-JUDGE: Really? So you prefer to die? You accept martyrdom?

Eyes wide open, lips trembling, Juliet says clearly:

JULIET: Yes. I accept.

Putting a finger to her chest, the girl adds:

GIRL-JUDGE: You still have time if you want salvation.

Loudly, proudly, her eyes sparkling with fanatic dedication, Juliet answers:

JULIET: Not the kind of salvation you speak of. I want that of my soul.

As an agreed-upon signal—forgetting to play their roles for one moment—the girl-soldiers raise Juliet by the armpits. Carefully and with difficulty, they carry her to a grating and tie her to it.

Obviously Juliet makes their job easy, stretching herself, very sweetly, on the grating, but she can't quite stop a grimace of pain from coming over her face when she is scratched by the sheet iron. Then the girl-soldiers put a wooden cross on her chest.

GIRL-JUDGE: Light the fire!

A lively-eyed little girl now starts up a fan that is hidden below the grating among many curlings of red paper that look like unmoving flames. The invisible fan makes the papers jump around so that they now seem like the flames of a lighted brazier.

The girl-soldiers carefully pull the rope of a huge windlass, their tongues between their teeth. And slowly they make the grating rise—the one on which Juliet is stretched out—toward the ceiling of the stage.

Another group of little girls, dressed in the white gowns of the catacombs—with the frightened, sincere expressions of the first flock of Christians—begins to sing, in very sweet voices, a very sweet song.

Laura is seen praying in the wings, praying that her friend Juliet may see God.

Stretched out on the grating, her hands tied, her neck tense and slightly raised, Juliet, very moved, looks down at the audience as it gets farther and farther away. On the stage, ten round mouths are raised high in sacred song, but Juliet's eyes are concentrated on the ceiling, which is slowly coming closer.

A great beatitude, augmented by the sweetness of the sacred song that rises from beneath her, fills her face. Her eyes express a fanatic faith, and she looks up to a precise point, as if awaiting a dazzling vision.

With difficulty, by pulling and twisting, Juliet frees her hands, and ecstatically she joins them—in a gesture of prayer—bringing the palms next to her chest.

The grating continues to rise shakily. Juliet, eyes bathed in tears, looks anxiously toward the large wooden shutters, which come ever closer to her and seem to unite the old ceiling to some awesome transcendency.

Hands joined together, Juliet holds herself in agonized expectation while two small reflectors, like those used in provincial theaters, hidden in the recesses of the ceiling, are suddenly lighted, bathing Juliet's face in an ecstatic, dazzling light. It really seems as if a divine, miraculous light—the kind of light that precedes or accompanies an apparition—had burst forth from the clouds.

Below, as the reflectors are lighted, the little girls, almost in unison, come forth with a long, satisfied, sincere, ingenuous "Ahhhhhh."

The audience, full of relatives and friends of the children, follows the ascension of the grating with suspenseful attention. Among the public, however, there is heard a muttering, and as the voice rises, it attracts general attention and much hushing. It is the voice of Juliet's grandfather, seated next to her mother and father. The old man moves around, moans, complains, and protests while Juliet's parents try in vain to keep him quiet. Seated farther forward, a red-bearded man, the principal, turns around and looks threateningly at the grandfather.

In the wings, Laura looks anxiously up at the grating, which has almost reached the ceiling. With her peaceful and sweet face, Juliet—covered with the gray makeup, which in the light looks like a death mask—watches and prays to the shutters, now very near.

JULIET: I am ready. Show me Your face. Take my heart, oh, Lord, I am ready. Sweet Lord, Jesus, let me see You now.

From below, during a pause in the song, mothers can be heard, moved, blowing their noses. But suddenly, in the midst of this transport, Juliet's grandfather rises, waving his arms, and shouts:

GRANDFATHER: Enough! This is indecent. Give me back my granddaughter. Juliet, come down. Obey me! (*He runs up to the stage, grabs the handle of the windlass, and turns it furiously, pushing away a nun who tries to stop him. Still turning the windlass violently, he shouts at the nuns.*) You go up this elevator, if you're not afraid of having us see your legs!

Everyone in the theater is standing up, shocked. Some shout; some protest. The mother superior, overwhelmed by the shock, gets up with a start and adjusts her monocle.

As a result of the energetic wrenching of the grandfather, the grating descends quickly, shaking frighteningly in space. Juliet, pale and dizzy, looks in all directions.

In the meantime, the grandfather, still moving the windlass, continues:

GRANDFATHER: What are you teaching these little girls? What do you want to do to these innocents? Put meat on your gratings!

In a shrill voice from the back of the room, the mother superior, close to fainting, calls out:

MOTHER SUPERIOR: Police! Call the police!

Some of the nuns, pale, fall on their knees in prayer, while, all together, like a flock of white aprons, the little girls sob loudly.

The old nun, hiding her wrinkled face in her hands, says in a deep voice:

OLD NUN: It's the end of the world.

The grandfather has finally succeeded in bringing the grating all the way down and energetically begins to untie Juliet, who looks at him without speaking.

He takes the halo from her head, revives her with loving slaps.

GRANDFATHER: And *you* don't say anything. You just let them do anything. Were you happy? Were you moved, idiot? Would you like to be roasted? (*He speaks to the others.*) Put a twelve-year-old girl in an oven! Play cannibals, you fools. Go to Africa if you like roast children. Or cook each other, you whores!

The principal goes to the front of the auditorium and thunders out to the grandfather in an indignant and severe voice:

PRINCIPAL: Professor de Filippis, in the name of God! Enough! Pull yourself together! End this shameful display. Do you hear me? I am your principal. You'll have to pay for this shameful, abominable scene.

Without paying attention, the grandfather tenderly helps Juliet down from the stage. With one hand, he takes her hand; with the other he tries to clean the gray makeup from her face.

LAURA (*crying*): Didn't you see Him? Didn't you see God?

Crying silently, crushed, Juliet lets herself be led away by her grandfather, but as she walks, she twists her face, and she looks upward at the closed shutters, which now are distant, with regret and disillusion. They are like a fading planet and become, beyond the bands of white light, darker and emptier.

JULIET'S GARDEN. EXTERIOR. DAYTIME.

The rays of the morning sun shine upon the trees and flowers. Juliet is seated, knitting.

From the bushes in front of her, a Persian cat appears mysteriously, a frivolous ribbon around its neck. Sliding, sinuous and soft, among the grass, the large cat comes over to Juliet, rubs against her right leg, and looks at her with enchanting, rather thoughtful golden eyes.

On the ribbon is written, as on excessively ornamental embroidery, one word only: *Susy*.

Juliet raises the cat to her knees, caresses it affectionately, looks deep into its golden eyes.

Standing up, having made a sudden decision, Juliet drops her knitting and, carrying the cat in her arms, heads toward the gate of Susy's villa.

THE GARDEN OF SUSY'S VILLA. EXTERIOR. DAYTIME.

The gate is half shut and—cat in arms—Juliet pushes it delicately and enters the rich garden. In the middle of the garden a shining, blue-tiled swimming pool surrounded by elegant outdoor furniture. With the cat held lovingly in her arms, Juliet timidly crosses the garden.

Scattered everywhere are the remains of a party. Abandoned party souvenirs, streamers, empty bottles. Everything very obvious, as if put there just to strike Juliet's imagination. A sense of total disorder under the covered terrace: many cushions still bearing the imprints of bodies, dirty dishes, records.

JULIET: May I—?

No one answers. Juliet enters the vast living room, a room full of all kinds of furniture, many sofas, curtains— disorder. Here the feeling of a party the night before is even stronger. A voice stops Juliet; it is Susy on the telephone. Though she would like to turn back, she is attracted by the voice and wants to listen. She stands, confused, in the veil of a curtain, which flutters around her face. She seems nailed there; she must listen.

Slowly, Susy's voice becomes clearer. A warm, sensual voice, interrupted by throaty laughter. A northern accent; from Ferrara.

> SUSY (*on the telephone*): No, no, no. I just got up; how do you think I am? You can imagine. . . . This spring. . . . What? Let me think a moment. The smell. Yes, your skin smells a little of tobacco and of salt water, the sea. I realized that, yes. (*She laughs.*) It was obvious—couldn't you tell from the way I laughed? (*She sighs.*) You're impossible. Today? Maybe late in the afternoon. . . . I'm letting myself go. . . . Yes, you're a rat. . . . No, no complications for me. . . . Everything, everything, but no complications. It must be simple, because it is simple. Like the first time. Yes? Yes? Yes! Go back to the shower; you'll catch cold. (*A long silence, Susy, with a smile on her lips, looks around lasciviously and sees Juliet. But, as if she hadn't seen her, she continues to smile into space.*) Yes. . . . Yes. . . . Yes. (*Susy's voice is increasingly excited. Softly, she says a final "yes."*) Hold on one minute. (*She puts the mouthpiece of the phone on the sofa where she had been stretched out and gets up, smiling at Juliet.*) Oh, how sweet; you brought Rubirosa back. (*The cat jumps out of Juliet's arms and goes to Susy, who picks it up, kisses and pets it.*) My Rubirosa. Enormous Ruby, here, here, to your sweet mistress who wants to have all of you. Oh, come on, my thief, my trouble-maker.

The cat miaows with pleasure. Without realizing it, Susy uses with him the same words she uses in her intimate mo-

ments with men; but she does it gracefully, in a low voice.
Under a transparent robe, Susy is naked; her hair is uncombed—but the presence of Juliet doesn't embarrass her
at all.

JULIET: He came into my garden. I thought I should
bring him back. You know, they steal them.

SUSY (*detached, cutting it short*): Thank you. Isn't it
true, Ruby, that we thank the lady? Imagine, they
might steal you! Thank you, signora. Signora—

JULIET: My name is Juliet.

SUSY: I'm Susy. You like my Rubirosa. You know, he
has a lot of names. Cloud, Pappone, Apollo—and,
finally, Lover. Yes! Oh . . . (*She picks up the phone
again.*) Are you still there? A woman who lives near
here brought Rubirosa back. . . . Beautiful? Of course.
(*She laughs.*) All my friends are beautiful. . . . Oh, that I
don't know. (*Quietly*) Maybe. . . . Good-bye, good-bye.
. . . Yes, yes, yes, yes. (*She hangs up the phone. Juliet
is pleased. She feels that by her mere presence in this
home she is living through an extraordinary adventure,
a little like a prostitute. Susy continues to talk.*) Oh,
how wonderful. Signora Juliet has come to bring the
big, beautiful cat home. Do you want anything, signora?
An apéritif?

JULIET (*hesitating, won over, finally accepting*): I don't
know. No. Yes.

Susy gets up, now playing the role of the perfect, dis-
tinguished hostess—with complete ease.

SUSY: Yes? Good. So do I. What would you like? I find
there is nothing better than a bottle of champagne. (*She
takes a bottle of champagne from the bar refrigerator
and expertly prepares to open it.*) Do you like it? Yes?
Do you know how to open it without letting all the
foam out? Look. Like this. (*She opens the smoking bottle perfectly.*) You see? Done. (*She fills two glasses,
gives one to Juliet.*) Chin-chin.

JULIET: Chin-chin.

Susy drinks with facetious greed.

> SUSY: Good . . . Do you like the service? (*She points to the two glasses.*) It's a special crystal. I never serve champagne in goblets. It's boorish. Some more?
> JULIET: No, thank you. It's delicious.

Noticing that Juliet is looking around her, Susy says:

> SUSY: If you want to see the house, come along. Come on. (*Preceding Juliet, Susy takes a bunch of gladioli from a vase, smells them a moment; then, noticing that they are not really fresh, she holds her nose.*) Brrr, how awful! They smell of death.

Susy throws the flowers into a basket and leads Juliet down a hallway.

On the walls are little paintings in doubtful taste. Little sketches, they represent—as in a profane, blasphemous *"Via Crucis"*—the successive seasons of the love life of a woman. They are little scenes, episodes, colored anecdotes of incredible erotic ardor. Stopping in front of them, nose in the air, a bit shocked but clearly interested, Juliet examines them carefully.

Impatient, from the end of the hallway, Susy calls out, lightly tapping her foot on the floor.

> SUSY: They're a gift from my fiancé. Filthy. But the men . . . (*She stops in front of a door and opens it. In the room, stretched out on a bed, is a dark girl.*) Marisa, how are you? You want to eat in bed? (*The girl doesn't answer, nor does she turn around. Susy puts the cat on her bed and kisses her.*) I'm leaving you, Rubirosa. (*She closes the door and returns to the hallway.*) You know, that girl wanted to kill herself. I saved her by a miracle. I telephoned and telephoned and there was no answer. We had to break down her door. I can't tell you how awful it was. Now I keep her here. Gianni —you'll meet him—makes a big play for her, which keeps her distracted.

JULIET: Like Laura—a friend of mine from school. She was only seventeen. They made it look like an accident. She drowned for love. Oh, look, from here you can see my house.

Juliet, from the balcony, looks at the modest little house lost in the trees. It looks almost ridiculous to her. She smiles, pensive.

SUSY: You two make me feel so tender when I see you. You're married, aren't you?

JULIET (*almost surprised*): Yes.

SUSY: I envy those who can do it; it must be beautiful —only one man. But how can it be done?

JULIET: It must also be beautiful to be free.

Susy opens a door onto a huge bedroom. A very low, wide bed, covered with delicate silk, contrasts with a thick dark-blue carpet. Susy falls gracefully on the bed and gestures Juliet to do the same. Reserved, rigid, dignified, Juliet sits on the edge of the bed, looking at the carpet—and at a pair of thick, furry men's slippers, which still seem warm from the feet of a man.

Susy's voice, over Juliet's shoulders, says quietly and cordially:

SUSY: Try to lie down.

Susy's affectionate and light hand urges Juliet down to the bed. Supine, Juliet looks up. A kind of silk curtain covers the ceiling above the bed. Susy pulls a cord, opening the curtain, and reveals, above, an enormous mirror, which reflects Juliet's face and body. With a repressed exclamation of shock, Juliet half rises, as if her own image had hit her. She looks, fascinated, into the mirror.

JULIET: Did you—find this here?

SUSY'S VOICE: Oh, no, I had it built in. Isn't it amusing? Sometimes I get the impression that there are four of us. Now who knows what you think of me? But, you know, men like to enjoy themselves.

Susy's voice suddenly fades away. Juliet turns to look for

her; she is gone. Her robe has been thrown on the bed. Only now does Juliet notice a large round hole in the floor, right next to the bed. From a distance there comes the muffled voice of Susy, together with a peculiar sound of rinsing.

SUSY'S VOICE: Juliet! Signora!

Juliet looks into the hole and sees, at the bottom of a long slide, the bluish movement of the waters of a pool. Susy, half naked, is swimming; she appears and disappears as in the glass of a telescope. Her happy voice rises from the water.

SUSY: Get undressed, and you come in, too. The water is warm. Just so that right after making love with my fiancé we can come down here just as we are. It's beautiful. We take a bath—and then we can start again. Come on, Juliet. Dive in.

DISSOLVE

CLOTHING STORE. INTERIOR. DAYTIME.

The inside of a fashionable boutique, with a large window overlooking the street. Susy's sports car is parked next to the sidewalk. Juliet and Susy get out of it. Several days have obviously passed since their first meeting, and Juliet has clearly succumbed to Susy's charms. Her hair is combed like Susy's; she elegantly wears a Chanel dress; she has a scarf twisted around her pocketbook. It is a new Juliet, well made up, imitating Susy even in her movements.

The street of this seaside town seems deserted, but the arrival of the two women has provoked a certain emotion in the salesmen and owners of nearby stores. They peer with curiosity into the boutique, to get a look at Susy, who always arouses interest. The owner of the store, a middle-aged woman—helped by a saleslady who does everything wrong and is also enchanted by Susy—moves toward the two customers, who come in laughing.

SUSY: My dear lady, do you have some nice little gifts—

you know, for a special party, something good—pins—belts—perfumes. I don't know—let's see something.
SHOPKEEPER: Right away, right away.

While the owner gives orders to the saleslady, she begins to take an infinite variety of boxes and objects from the window and from the shelves and to put them on a table. Outside, a young man, pushed rather violently against the window by someone we don't see, appears. Susy, reserved, goes to the mirror to look at herself, followed at once by Juliet. Susy grimaces at the mirror and then says:

SUSY (*to Juliet*): You know, you really look better; you're really pretty! What does your husband say? Does he notice the difference?
JULIET: Well, he comes home late . . . in the evening.
SUSY: Did you put on the robe with feathers?
JULIET: It's too much.
SUSY: Try it and give me a whistle. (*They both laugh. Susy goes to the counter and picks out some things, very sure of herself.*) This! This! For Marisa, perfume. This is fine. How many men have we? Let's say a dozen. Let's get a dozen ties, each in a separate package. They won't ever wear them, anyway. Oh, this pin. Give me five lire, Juliet. This I'm giving you right now. Look how lovely. It's Dior. (*Juliet would like to protest, but Susy has already put the pin on her collar.*) It looks good, doesn't it? And look at that kimono. What strength! (*She points to a Japanese kimono, goes to take it, puts it in front of her, and looks at herself in the mirror.*) Too short. But it would be perfect on you, Juliet. Try it on. (*Juliet again wants to protest, but Susy pushes her toward the mirror while giving instructions to the shopkeeper.*) Pretty packages, with bows. And a good discount. I'm paying cash. At least twenty percent. Otherwise we'll have a battle.

The shopkeeper protests weakly, but hurriedly joins the saleslady in putting the various objects in boxes and wrapping them up. The saleslady moves dreamily.

Outside, on the street, are young men, attracted by the spectacle of Susy, though pretending to stand there to get the sun.

A young man from Sardinia or some such place appears, jumping with joy because they have told him that two beautiful women are in the store.

Inside, Juliet takes off her bolero to try on the kimono.

SUSY: The blouse, too.

Susy laughingly pulls the screen that separates the fitting room from the rest of the store. From the sidewalk, murmurs of disappointment from the young men. Susy laughs. Juliet decides to take off the blouse, too and is left with a brassiere. She puts on the kimono; it does look well on her. From behind, Susy pulls the corners of Juliet's eyebrows to make her look Japanese. Lightly, jokingly, always saying the right thing, Susy says:

SUSY (*quietly*): I'm giving this to you, too. But you have to promise that you'll wear it.
JULIET: No, it's too much.
SUSY: You must become a vamp. You must walk over a floor of ardent lovers. In the meantime, I'm going to try on a sweater. (*She quickly takes off her bolero. Underneath, she is naked, with a thin, half-moon brassiere. She takes a white scarf and puts it over her face so as not to ruin her makeup. As she tries on a long sweater of very soft wool, she continues to talk.*) Men—they say nothing matters to them. How women dress. But how they fall for everything! They feel the difference right away. The cloth, the silk, the quality—and a little perfume just in the right places. They claim they have such respect for simple women, but how much more they have for the whores! (*Juliet looks surprised while Susy continues to speak from behind the scarf, like an ectoplasm.*) And, of course, they don't have to be whores, just imitate them. Or be just like them, but with class. Give him the feeling you do everything just for

him. They want this, but also let them know that we
can do it for others. Oh, yes. This makes them behave.

She takes the scarf from her face and looks into the mirror. She is beautiful. The sweater makes her look like a musical comedy chorus girl. She smiles boastfully, takes Juliet
by the arm and swings her around. They laugh like two
clowns.

THE STREET OUTSIDE THE STORE. EXTERIOR. DAYTIME.

Juliet and Susy, loaded down with packages, leave the
store. They are enveloped by a gust of wind. They laugh,
hold on to a lamp post as if to resist the wind, almost play-
fully. Susy fights to keep her skirt down, and the two of
them laugh loudly.

STREET AND CAR. EXTERIOR. DAYTIME.

The car, driven by Susy, goes along the street at moderate
speed. Juliet is talking while Susy is curiously silent.

JULIET: For me, marriage has always been this way. I
am all his; he is all mine, and only mine, forever. What
can I do? I've always thought of marriage like that. Do
you understand?
SUSY: Like that? Yes.

In the meantime, Susy looks in the rear-view mirror. A
car, driven by a young man, is following Susy's. Susy seems
to pay no attention, and Juliet goes on talking.

JULIET: They always spoke of it like that. I didn't look
for anything else. My husband, our home . . .

After another quick look in the rear-view mirror, Susy
pulls over to a gas station and stops in front of a pump.
She gives the keys to the attendant and asks for three thousand lire worth of high-test. The car that had been following
hers stops on the other side of the pump, just opposite

Susy's. In it there is a dark, handsome young man whose eyes devour Susy. She looks him straight in the eye and then looks elsewhere, apparently with complete indifference. Juliet misses all this; she follows her own thoughts, almost speaking to herself.

> JULIET: Because Giorgio was—I'm almost ashamed to say it—he was my first love. When he asked me to marry him, I could hardly believe it. (*Susy starts her car up again, and the other one follows at once. Juliet finally realizes it.*) But that car—it's following us.
>
> SUSY (*neither surprised nor disturbed*): That one . . . yes.
>
> JULIET: Do you know him?
>
> SUSY: Never seen him before. (*Then, suddenly, with a laugh*) You don't know how many times it's been a woman who's followed me!
>
> JULIET (*finding this hard to understand*): A woman?
>
> SUSY: It's incredible, but women, too, look at me a lot. Women must like your Giorgio very much, don't they?

Juliet's voice is both disturbed and full of unconditional admiration.

> JULIET: He's so handsome. For me he's been everything. Husband, father, lover. Everything. A man like that—who takes you away with him, gives you a home, his name, loves you, protects you . . . (*Susy has speeded up the car and stops it almost with a jolt in front of Juliet's gate. She looks at Juliet, waiting for her to get out.*) Ah, we're here. Come in—we'll have some tea and talk a little more.

Susy becomes almost rude; she is tense and hurried. Opening the door on Juliet's side, she says:

> SUSY: Now? I'm expecting a call from Momi, my fiancé. I'm sorry. Later, maybe. Or tomorrow. (*Juliet gets out and, in doing so, realizes that the car that has been following them is still there, waiting at the corner. Susy*

closes the door and begins to drive on.) So long. I'll call you.

Juliet doesn't even have time to say good-bye. She sees Susy stop the car a bit farther ahead, at her own gate. Susy gets out of the car, enters the gate and leaves it slightly ajar. Juliet, too, enters the pathway of her garden. Suddenly understanding, she stops and looks behind her.

The young man has gotten out of his car. He slowly approaches Susy's gate.

Susy appears on the terrace for a moment.

The young man throws away his cigarette and pushes the gate decisively.

Juliet, stares, dismayed.

JULIET'S HOME. INTERIOR. DAYTIME.

A morning, just like the preceding one.

Juliet has just arisen. She is in the bedroom, in her robe. Combing her hair distractedly, she looks at herself in the mirror from several angles.

In the kitchen, Fortunata is cleaning the vegetables. She speaks to herself, whining.

Juliet goes to the window and looks out. All is silent, tranquil, still.

The lawn is full of waiting cats. Small ones, big ones, very small ones, white, black, black-and-white, yellowish, gray, gray-and-white—they all look toward the house. Upon seeing Juliet, many of them get up; they move their tails and miaow.

Juliet moves back from the window and goes to the living room, calling out halfheartedly:

JULIET: Fortunata.
FORTUNATA'S VOICE: Signora.
JULIET: The cats are waiting. (*She slowly goes to the kitchen.*) They're all there. Did Michelina bring the fish?
FORTUNATA: Yes, signora.
JULIET: Where is it?

Fortunata gives her a large package containing fish heads

and tails. Juliet opens the door that leads to the garden, and at once a mob of cats, tails shaking, whiskers tense, come running in a comic battle of pantomime and miaows.

Juliet, helped by Fortunata, begins giving out the food. Both work seriously and conscientiously.

JULIET: Careful. That one is terrible. He'll eat it all himself. Stay back. Keep some for the blind one. Look at the little—(*She realizes that Fortunata is whimpering.*) What's wrong? What's come over you? Look at that one there, look at that gangster. And who is that one? I never saw him before. Who are you? Look how the others are sniffing. They don't want him. Give him something. But, Fortunata, what's the matter? You're not by any chance pregnant again, are you? Again? Oh, young lady . . . How many are there now? Seven? Look, be careful. You just can't—it's not possible. How many months?

FORTUNATA: Three. And now you'll send me away.

JULIET: No, I won't. Have I ever sent you away? It's the fourth time this has happened since you came here. I say it for your own good. (*She grabs a lively cat who has run into the kitchen.*) Out. Out of there. Look how impudent he is! It's always that one. Some day I have to speak to your husband. (*The phone rings in the living room; Juliet goes to answer it, still talking to Fortunata.* In ten years, seven children. Like a machine. No . . . (*She talks into the phone.*) Hello. . . . Yes, speaking. . . . Yes, of course. . . . ah. . . . ah. . . . ah. . . . Now? Right away? . . . Within half an hour. . . . But it hasn't even been a week, you know. . . . Ah. . . . ah . . . ah. . . . Yes. . . . Yes. . . . There's something— Ah. . . . ah. . . . yes. (*She puts down the telephone; frightened and lost, she is unable to think. Then suddenly she picks up the phone and, with trembling hands, dials a number.*) Hello, Adele? . . . What? . . . Ah? . . . What number is this? . . . I'm sorry. (*She slams down the receiver.*) Damn it, what is the number? Oh, yes. (*Weakly she dials another number.*) Hello, Adele? . . . Call Adele. . . . Not in. . . . Ah. . . . No, no. Thank you. (*She hangs up. Frightened, she dials the same number again, rapidly.*) Hello. . . . Yes. . . . Have her call me at once, as soon as she gets back. (*She hangs up, then tries to pull herself together and dials another number.*) Hello, Valentina? . . . Who is it . . . Raniero? . . . Not in? Where did she go? . . . Ah. . . . ah. . . . No, thanks. Excuse me. Good-bye. (*She hangs up and then realizes she is still in her robe; one more worry.*) What time is it?

She runs into the kitchen. There Fortunata is singing—reassured and out of tune. The cats surround her.

Juliet goes to the bedroom and changes her clothes. She puts her skirt on the wrong way, can't find her shoes, and then, when she does, puts them on the wrong way. She has a knit sweater over her head when the doorbell rings. Juliet shouts:

JULIET: Fortunata! Let him in. I'm coming right away.

She feverishly finishes dressing and combing her hair. Then she goes into the living room.

A middle-aged man, with little curls around his bald scalp, dressed like an undertaker, is standing upright in the middle of the room. He has a thick portfolio and also a large box. He displays a courtesy that doesn't seem to suit him. When speaking those words that seem the most compromising, he lowers his voice and twists his mouth, throwing suspicious glances toward the door, like a conspirator. When he sees Juliet, he bows deeply and kisses her hand.

Juliet is especially interested in the thick portfolio and the large box. She sits down silently; the man sits next to her after having asked her permission. He then gets up again to offer her a cigarette, which she silently refuses.

AGENT: Cigarette? (*He then takes one for himself and sits down again.*) May I? Does the smoke bother you? (*Juliet shakes her head. The man lowers his voice.*) Can I talk? There's no one here? (*Juliet nods her head. The man opens the portfolio and takes out a number of documents.*) The notes on our spying. (*He lowers his voice on the word "spying."*) Five consecutive days, with the same results. (*He opens the files, hands them to Juliet, pointing out things and summarizing.*) The subject regularly frequents a person who lives at number forty-five, via Archimede, stairway B, apartment seven. He usually stays there between two and five in the afternoon. He stops the car near the building at about eight in the evening; the person joins him, and they frequent fashionable restaurants. They come home at about eleven, and the subject stays in the apartment until about one. The night of the twenty-fifth, until three. The person whom the subject frequents is named Gabriella Olson; twenty-four years old; a model by profession; Swedish. (*The agent, who has lowered his voice upon pronouncing the name Gabriella, lowers it again as he repeats it, holding out a photo.*) Gabriella Olson. Note the clarity of the picture. Taken with our special telephoto lens, from thirty meters—from the terrace across the way. We can see the smallest details, even this little mark on her left cheek. Here is Gabriella Olson in her apartment with the subject. The subject is not easily distinguishable because there is a curtain in the way. The pose seems suspicious. Here is the subject in the company of Olson, leaving forty-five via Archimede. Here is the subject, accompanied by Olson, leaving the restaurant Passetto at eleven o'clock. Night light, but perfect execution. Here the face of the subject is clearly recognizable. The photographic documentation is both rich and complete. (*He opens the large box, looks around, gets up.*) Is there an outlet here, please? No, please, excuse me; I'll do it. (*He attaches the box to an electrical outlet, explaining.*) This is a tape recorder, like those used by the American police. We can tune in from a distance of thirty meters. Conversation intercepted while the two subjects were stopping in the car near Porta Pinciana, at about ten-thirty last night. (*He turns a key, and the tape begins to move. Most of the words are unclear, mingled with street noises and other background sounds.*)

TAPE RECORDER: Why? . . . evening I am tired . . . darling . . . at the hairdresser tomorrow morning . . . absolutely . . . careful . . . let's go home . . . (*For a few seconds the voices are heard distinctly.*) Want so badly to sleep near you. . . . Darling, dearest, if you could only stay until tomorrow. (*Again the sounds of cars, and then something that sounds like kissing, and finally a harsh braking that overpowers any other sounds.*)

JULIET'S ROOM. INTERIOR. EVENING.

Juliet is alone in the bedroom, motionless before the window; there is total silence.

Then, in the sky, just over the pines, a jet passes, preparing to land at the nearby airport.

Juliet, as if wanting to shake off her feeling of solitude and darkness, turns on all the lights and looks around the room.

She opens the closet. On the hangers are Giorgio's suits and a bathrobe. With a brusque gesture of the hand, she moves these clothes to the back of the closet, almost hiding them. Then, whistling loudly with heart-rending determination, she goes to the double bed. Giorgio's pillow is on one side. Juliet grabs it, squeezes it with her fists, and throws it aside, putting her own pillow in the middle of the bed.

She is suddenly very tired, with a great desire to go to sleep, to forget everything. She takes off her dress, pulling it hurriedly over her head. She stands in her slip, in the bright illumination of the room. She looks at herself in the mirror in the blinding reflection of the lights—her arms hanging sadly at her sides.

She is suddenly depressed; her eyes fill with tears. She tries to straighten her back, raises her shoulders.

But the image now reflected in the mirror is not a consoling one. She painfully examines herself. Now she blames only herself for her husband's defection; she is left without hope.

The noise of jazz music comes from Susy's garden; many cars can be heard arriving.

Susy is obviously having a party. Juliet turns her head decisively.

In her slip, she goes to the window and looks out, hiding herself behind the white silk curtain. Tightening her lips as if ready for a blunt and sudden challenge, she pulls away from the window and opens the closet. Under the reddish light of the closet she examines the row of cocktail dresses.

Juliet quickly takes an elegant flame-red dress, the most low-cut she has, and brings it in front of the mirror, preparing to put it on.

While her body disappears inside the flaming red outline of the lamé dress. Juliet hums to herself, her brow wrinkled in angry challenge.

JULIET: Boys, if I put my mind to it, who's more whorish than I am?

THE GARDEN OF SUSY'S VILLA. EXTERIOR. EVENING

Juliet, in her red dress, approaches the gate to Susy's villa. She is excited, expectant; she is about to face something important and decisive.

The garden looks splendid, fabulous. Colored lights are everywhere. Illuminated jets pour forth like sumptuous foliage. Waiters in white jackets either serve the guests or stand solemnly next to the monumental open-air buffet, where tall castles of sandwiches are placed next to marvelous lobsters and roast pheasants, lined up wing to wing on the table like sumptuous trophies.

Ravishing in her magnificent cocktail dress, light as a caress, sparkling with jewels, Susy comes over to greet Juliet, who stops, confused. Susy beckons to a waiter who is carrying a tray full of glasses and liquor bottles around the room.

SUSY: Wonderful that you came. What will you drink? The same as mine again?

She puts a glass full of red liquid in Juliet's hand and

takes the same for herself. She sips the drink, her eyes full of the sheer joy of living.

Juliet gulps down half the drink, hoping the liquor will help her overcome her despair. A bit stunned, but refreshed, she asks:

JULIET: It's delicious. What's it called?
SUSY: I invented it myself. It should be called a Susy. (*Finishing her drink, she goes on brusquely but good-naturedly.*) I'll teach you how to make it some other time. Come along now.

She takes Juliet by the hand, most attentively; then, as if she had suddenly remembered something, she asks:

SUSY: But your husband—the handsome one—where is he? You must keep him hidden. Did you send him to bed without supper?

Shrugging her shoulders, with a false boldness and an exaggerated joy, Juliet says:

JULIET: He won't be back this evening. Work, work, always work. He always sends me out alone. He has faith in me.

Susy looks at Juliet affectionately but inquisitively. She has the intelligent look of someone who has understood everything.

SUSY: He's doing the wrong thing!

Susy then leads Juliet from one group to another: bronzed faces, warm smiles, cordial greetings; they all form an exciting barrier that is sweetly opened by Susy's steps.

In a delightful state of euphoria, Juliet—taking one drink after another, fearlessly and recklessly mixing them—follows Susy, who has a brilliant, witty word for everyone, pronouncing a last name here, a first name there, as if to reveal to Juliet the mysteries of a fascinating community.

Susy comes to a very handsome young man, with a sincere smile and the indolent look of an athlete. Susy turns him around as if he were a model and shows him to Juliet.

SUSY: Show the lady your beautiful chest, Valerio. Look, Juliet. The body is the only good thing about him. But, I promise you, that's not a small thing. (*She winks and speaks to the young man.*) If this lady whistles for you, run immediately. I warn you—don't keep her waiting.

Juliet, though tempted to show herself full of desire, lowers her eyes, blushing, then raises them, and, trying to show ardor, says:

JULIET: Unfortunately, I don't know how to whistle.

Susy bursts into happy laughter.

SUSY: It doesn't matter. He'll come even if you don't whistle.

She stops Juliet a moment under a light and gently passes a finger under her eye. She looks at her intelligently.

SUSY: You're very strange this evening. And your eyes are red. What is it? Have you been crying?

Juliet shrugs her shoulders and moves quickly away from her.

JULIET: What do you mean, crying? I couldn't be happier. It's the eye makeup, that's all.

Susy says, taking her by the arm and moving her away from the light:

SUSY: All the better. Everything seems just right for me, too, tonight. There's not one person I don't like—not here, anyway.

Approaching a tall, thin man with a hollow, bronzed face and clear, bright eyes, Susy, with a special voice that makes Juliet understand just who this is, says:

> SUSY: Juliet, this is my fiancé. Momy, dear, this is Juliet, my delightful neighbor.

Juliet gives him her hand, which he kisses rather coolly. She would like to say something to him, but Susy takes her by the arm with the excuse of bringing her to the buffet and says excitedly:

> SUSY: What did you think of him? It's him, you understood that?

Taking a piece of lobster, Juliet says with sincerity and compassion, as to a sister:

> JULIET: He's handsome. He's nice, and he's a gentleman.
> SUSY: And you know how old he js? Guess! He was just seventy.
> JULIET (*almost incredulous*): It's not possible. Seventy! No, I don't believe it. It's too much.

Happy, pleased in her excitement, as if she were praising the excellence of a son, Susy says:

> SUSY: I swear it. And, you know, he makes love better than young men do. He has the wind of a boy of twenty.

She winks at Juliet, suddenly looking very much like Iris. She then moves away with an innocent, almost animal-like impudence, leaving Juliet bewildered, a plate of lobster in her hand.

A strange light, partially hidden by a group of people, attracts her to a corner of the garden. There one of the guests is projecting very bright slides, which reflect bright colors on the pure white walls of the villa and, above all, on the white dresses of two laughing girls who, leaning against the wall, act as an obedient screen.

Attracted as if to the magic of a window to a new world, Juliet joins the seven or eight people who make up the fascinated group.

A man who seems to be an important photographer describes the slides as they are shown.

PHOTOGRAPHER: The nervation of a leaf.

A young guest comments happily:

YOUNG GUEST: A fig leaf, we hope.

The photographer changes the slide. Now it is like the gilded surface of a lunar crater seen from the earth. It hits the wall and the white dresses of the girls.

PHOTOGRAPHER: Sand on the palm of a hand.

The lunar crater is, however, shown right in the center of the bosom of one of the girls. When she realizes it, she shouts in horror, modestly covering her bosom with her hands; a gesture of Aphrodite.

ANOTHER GUEST: Too bad; it was in just the right place.

Juliet looks at the projection and laughs, moving forward in the group.

The photographer changes the slide. Now a very bright light illuminates what looks like a number of immense stems, openings outstretched, as if turgid with desire, coming from the depths of a gigantic shell. The image falls on the round belly of one of the laughing girls.

The photographer, calm and professional, but very pleased, says:

PHOTOGRAPHER: Pistils in the interior of a corolla.

An old man moves to the front of the group, next to Juliet; he says, half seriously:

OLD MAN: Learn, girls, how to ask for the seed. Aren't those excited pistils more expressive than any face, than a tense mouth?

A close-up of Juliet who looks at these figures of desperate, vital desire. Through the trees, over the brightness of the colored slides, there comes the sound of an orchestra, giddy with happiness, playing—in the confusing, joyous rhythm of the Surf—"If I Had a Hammer."

With another glass of liquor in hand, Juliet goes toward the floor. There she watches, fascinated, a girl in black slacks and blouse, long black hair over her shoulders, who is dancing on the green tiles, shaking all over, raising her arms in complicated responses, in graceful provocations, with strong movements of the pelvis, the loins, the knees.

Passing in front of Juliet, the girl—still shaking to the rhythm of the Surf—says with a marked German accent and a strident voice:

GIRL: Beautiful lady. Don't you like to dance?

Very timid and surprised, Juliet realizes that the girl strongly resembles the picture of Gabriella that she has seen.

JULIET: Yes. But I don't know this dance.

She raises her head and, almost hopefully, looks at the girl, who, beckoning, wags her finger and—still dancing—says to her:

GIRL: Go on! Come here!

Juliet laughs and shakes her head. A waiter passes, carrying a tray of drinks, and she takes one, gulping it down. It burns her throat and makes her blink her eyes.

She now finds herself in the middle of the floor, in front of the girl. Half drunk, she tries to imitate—awkwardly, but with great verve—the movement of the Surf that the girl makes.

Still dancing, the girl says to her in a rough, guttural voice:

GIRL: Answer me with movement, please.

The girl is shaking with the wild rhythm, hands raised high. Juliet shakes in front of her, precisely imitating her, just as one should do with the Surf.

Now the girl raises her right hand, seemingly cracking a whip, goading a horse at full speed that, racing, carries her away—the classic movement of the Surf.

Overwhelmed by a bitter and desperate intoxication, Juliet, too, shakes, raising her right hand, her imaginary whip. The repeated gesture seems to make her happy, more intoxicated.

Still dancing, she asks the girl:

JULIET: Do you know someone named Gabriella? (*In a close-up, the girl's eyes are half closed. She shrugs her shoulders as if to say she didn't understand. Juliet, now completely drunk, still dancing, looks up at the girl, almost shouting.*) Gabriella! Gabriella Olson?

Distracted, nodding her head purely out of courtesy and giving no guarantee that her answer is an honest one, the girl says:

GIRL: Gabriella ... *ja.*

Still dancing clumsily, Juliet desperately takes the girl's hand and shouts:

JULIET: She's beautiful, isn't she?
GIRL (*still dancing and not looking at Juliet*): Very beautiful. *Ja.*

Juliet goes on with wild joy.

JULIET: More beautiful than I am, isn't she?

The girl, now like an idol roused by Dionysian rhythm, doesn't answer. She dances with her eyes almost closed, her lips sealed.

Juliet stops dancing and jumps in front of her, squeezing her hand.

> JULIET (*with an almost ferocious sob*): She's more of a whore. Say it: She's much more of a whore than I am.

This time the girl stops. She looks at Juliet, eyes wide open, horrified.

Now a young man comes up from the back and picks up the girl, raising her in his arms, putting his face to her behind and saying loudly:

> YOUNG MAN: Enough, Hilda. We don't want any more girls in slacks on the floor. Either you undress completely or you get off the floor.

Juliet remains alone. She goes to the edge of the floor where she can look at the frenetically dancing couples.

Her eyes fix on the members of the orchestra, who are playing loudly as if discharging a great outburst of electricity with savage joy.

A Negro musician—young and handsome—raises his trumpet and begins a frantic solo. Standing steadily against the starry sky, his young, athletic body, hard and muscular, is profiled under his red tuxedo, while the trumpet, raised in his hands, seems to hold him in a phallic triumph.

Juliet slowly approaches the orchestra, looking up at this delirious musician, free as a wild divinity.

Little by little, all the guests stop dancing and gather round to listen to the solo. But Juliet is in front of all of them, physically overcome by this wave of sound, her face contracted, her eyes shining.

The young musician, too, notices her. Tossing off his tremendous cascade of notes, he winks at her, happily, while his trumpet, in the refraction of the spotlights, sends blinding, flashing lights all around.

The music stops. The musician puts his trumpet on the

piano and remains, looking at Juliet. She, in turn, deeply moved by such splendor, by the beauty of the musician, is choked up; she smiles at him.

The pianist, in white, somewhat effeminate, tries to start a conversation to break the spell. He turns to the trumpet player.

> PIANIST (*in English*): Let's have a drink. You want something, Tom?

The trumpet player makes a calm negative gesture with his hand. He asks Juliet softly:

> TRUMPET PLAYER (*in English*): Did you like it?
> JULIET (*seriously*): I wished it would never end.

The trumpet player turns to the pianist, asking for a translation.

> PIANIST: She says she wished it would never end. She's easily pleased. Sweet.

The trumpet player thanks Juliet, slowly shaking his head. He gets up with a sigh and goes to pour himself a drink.

During the silence that follows, Susy sits down at the piano and begins to play very softly on the low notes; then she starts "Tea for Two" and suddenly asks Juliet, pointing to the trumpet player:

> SUSY: You like him? (*There is a pensive smile on Juliet's face. Susy goes on.*) Don't you think he's a marvelous specimen? All black silk. And he seems the type who can be had, don't you think? (*The trumpet player looks back and forth between Susy and Juliet.*) I even feel jealous. Come on, Juliet, a sincere opinion. What do you think?
> JULIET (*choked up*): He's very . . . very . . .

She shrugs her shoulders, not knowing what to say.

SUSY: Sexy, you mean. Yes, that's it—no use searching for a word. And he's even shy, which is best of all. Imagine! If you weren't my friend, I'd do everything to— But it wouldn't do any good. He wants you. He doesn't stop looking at you. (*Decisively.*) Why don't you show him around the house? (*Susy stops playing. She is speaking seriously. Now, from Juliet's reaction, she will know whether or not to go with this friendship.*) He follows you around like a little dog. My room is free. (*She sounds like the madam of a whorehouse. Juliet glances around, frightened, with a worn smile. She is afraid someone may have heard. Susy turns to the trumpet player and speaks in English.*) Wouldn't you like to freshen up, take a shower? (*He nods his head, and Susy turns hurriedly to Juliet.*) You see. Go with him. Show him the way. The party can't last a year. You have to make up your mind. And think of *him*. Who knows where *he* is tonight?

Juliet is resolved. With some effort, she nods her head in agreement. She gets up. Susy is looking at her as if to say: You won't make it; you're a poor little middle-class wife, only capable of complaining about your husband's infidelities. She laughs ironically. But Juliet answers:

JULIET (*to the trumpet player*): Let's go.

She precedes him to the stairway and begins to ascend. Susy starts to play the piano again. In the half shadow of the room, from the darkness of the stairway that Juliet and the trumpet player are climbing, a group is seen gathered around the photographer. Voices and laughter are heard.

Juliet walks through the hallway, silently followed by the trumpet player. They go into Susy's room. The window is open, and the breeze swells the curtains.

The young trumpet player, suddenly a little boy, sits down on the bed and looks up at the ceiling, where the enormous mirror reflects his image. He leans over toward Juliet, only lightly touching her with one hand. Shyly, with a childish and gay smile, he says, pointing to the mirror:

TRUMPET PLAYER: Look there. We're together as if on a cloud; the two of us, up there.

Opening her eyes with difficulty, heavy with sleep and dizziness, Juliet asks, as if she were a thousand miles away:

JULIET: What?

But the trumpet player, with his childish smile, continues to point toward the mysterious luminosity of the mirror.

Juliet, suddenly embarrassed, looks up and sees their two shapes, one next to the other, rendered almost supernatural and abstract by the mysterious perspective of the mirror.

Suddenly a huge flame flares up in the mirror and a burning wreath is superimposed on the reflected image, piercing it with lightning, almost obliterating it.

An enormous grating, in flames, with a mystical figure of a woman tied on it, occupies all the light of the mirror.

With a cry of terror, Juliet runs away from the bed.

SUSY'S GARDEN. EXTERIOR. EVENING.

Crying, screaming out disconnected words, Juliet rushes out to the garden, crosses it hurriedly, bumping into guests and knocking over a tray.

The orchestra stops playing; the couples stop dancing. Susy tries to catch Juliet, who is looking for a way out.

SUSY: Juliet, stop! Where are you going? What happened?

Struggling, Juliet pulls away and runs toward the exit, shouting:

JULIET: Let me go. I'm going. I won't stay any longer. I'll never come back here!

She opens the gate and goes out into the dark of the pine forest. The sound of voices and the multicolored reflections of the lights are lost in the distance.

PINE FOREST. EXTERIOR. NIGHT.

Sobbing, Juliet runs through the woods, trying one path after another, losing herself, awakening and frightening birds as she flees.

Above, over the curtain of pines, there arises in reddish splendor a gigantic vision of the flaming grating—like an aurora borealis.

Above that, beyond the foliage of the trees, visible and unearthly as the moon, is the face of the martyr, exuding sweat and blood, staring at Juliet, smiling at her horribly.

Juliet stops, sobbing convulsively. She falls to her knees on the grass, her forehead touching the earth. Crying, she makes the sign of the cross—once, twice, three times—kissing the dew-covered earth as she does.

JULIET'S GARDEN. EXTERIOR. DAYTIME.

Afternoon. The setting sun sends oblique blades of light through the pines and through the trees in the garden.

Many people are in the garden, all immobile, as if on painted enamel.

Juliet's mother, seated in a beach chair, is talking to Adele.

Juliet's husband is seated in another beach chair, a little farther on. He is surrounded by Adele's children and is entertaining them with a magic trick. Also present are Don Raffaele and his wife, Alba, Chierichetta, a new muscle man, Valentina, and Raniero are standing in the distance. They are listening to an agitated talk given by a very ugly young man, full of tics. He is a psychoanalyst. On the tables are tea, whiskey, etc., which are being passed.

Juliet is seated on the arm of a chair, alone, though in the midst of the others. Her hair is almost uncombed; she wears no makeup and looks bewildered. She watches her husband with a mixture of guilt and suspicious alarm while he shows the children the miracle of a glassful of water, covered only by a sheet of paper, that doesn't empty when turned upside down.

GIORGIO: We cover it. . . . Watch carefully. . . . There's

only this little piece of paper. . . . One, two, three—I turn it upside down. Nothing. The water doesn't pour out. The glass is still full.

He throws the water away, laughing at the admiring astonishment of the children. He looks quickly at his watch, then looks toward Juliet, who pretends she has not noticed. Solicitous, she offers him something to drink.

JULIET: Another whiskey?

Giorgio answers very politely, then immediately turns to the children, as if looking for an alibi.

GIORGIO: No, thanks, dear. Now I'll do another trick. Let's take three matches . . .

Juliet moves away from Giorgio, going over to her mother and sister, but she does throw another glance in his direction, just in time to see him again looking at his watch.
Her mother and sister continue their intimate conversation. Juliet stands behind her mother and slowly, as if to come between the two, begins to arrange her mother's hair, admiringly. Every once in a while she looks over at her husband, disturbed, defeated.

MOTHER: . . . her husband went to get her, but she didn't want to. Imagine Giovanna! She called Marisa right away. In addition, she had the child with the flu, and Teresa had gone home.
ADELE: Yes, but she and Luciana are such good friends—
MOTHER: Her mother is awful. And they take care of the house together! (*Annoyed, she speaks to Juliet.*) What are you doing? Ruining my hair. (*She starts again.*) In the meantime, the child was born—five and a half pounds—
ADELE: Two pounds less than Luisella.
MOTHER: Basically, what do I care? It's their business. Enrico has already sold his car.

The mother's voice is overpowered by a deep noise, the sound of distant, approaching drums. Juliet turns toward the gate. Above it is the face of the savage enemy, intent on spying in the garden. He is an explorer. On horseback, he has hoisted himself up in his stirrups to look inside the garden.

Juliet turns her head toward the other side of the fence. Beyond it she sees another savage horseman galloping silently around the garden.

In the meantime, the first one—who for one moment had stared into Juliet's eyes—sits in his saddle again, and his head disappears; a glimpse is seen of the horseman galloping away.

Valentina's group has slowly come toward Juliet. The young doctor next to her, still very ugly and full of tics, is saying, with obsessive gesticulation:

> PSYCHOANALYST: "I must cross the frontier, but no one will tell me where it is. I see a small light, and I suppose it is the customs inspector's hut. But suddenly someone grabs me like a madman." Second dream: "I have to cross the frontier—more than that, I have already crossed it and am in the little customs station. I have only a little bag, but the inspector opens it and takes from it two mattresses." The etiology of the nervous resistance had nothing to do with this. Rather, it was a matter of anticipatory dreams.
>
> ALBA: But the phallic symbol has a concrete meaning, doesn't it? What archetype is it?

The group moves on slowly. Raniero is looking for ice, but there seems to be no more. The mother says to Juliet:

> MOTHER: I told you to let me alone. Look, there's no more ice.

Juliet moves away, takes the empty ice bucket, and goes to the house. Her mother continues to look at her and calls to her:

> MOTHER: What's the matter with you? You're more

green than ever. Put on a little makeup, comb your
hair. You really are green-looking.

Juliet throws a glance at her husband, who, now unobserved and alone, yawns.

She goes into the house.

JULIET'S HOUSE. INTERIOR. DAYTIME.

Juliet enters the house and goes to the refrigerator in the
kitchen. She opens it, takes out the ice cubes, and puts them
in the bucket. For a few seconds, in the brief sparkle of the
ice cubes, two long and beautiful legs, in net stockings, seem
to appear. Juliet quickly looks away from the cubes. With
bucket in hand, she goes to the bedroom. As if to verify what
her mother said, she looks at herself in the large mirror. She
takes a comb and goes closer to the mirror.

The large sheet of glass clearly reflects the image of Iris.
Juliet, startled, turns instinctively over her shoulder to look
for Iris, but the room is empty.

Suddenly, pulling herself together, she half opens the
closet. Inside it, smiling at her ironically, is Iris. Juliet quickly closes the door, but the voice of Iris follows her.

IRIS'S VOICE: Juliet . . . Juliet.

Juliet doesn't turn around; she goes into the living room.
There is Iris, arranging flowers in a vase, with her usual
grace and ability.

IRIS: I began to make love when I was thirteen. There
was a handsome man I liked. A handsome man of about
thirty. One morning I entered his bedroom. He was in
bed. (*She laughs a little.*) Temperament, my dear.
JULIET: Go away. Leave me in peace. Liar! Whore!
IRIS (*not at all upset*): You see how gladioli should be arranged? This way. But then, what do I care? Tonight I
sing at the Bal Tabarin, and then I dine with my lover,
who adores me.

Iris disappears.
Juliet starts to leave, but Iris comes back.

IRIS: No, I'm not the liar. The liar is the other one, the one in the flames. The fire is Hell, don't you know that? Idiot. If you had done it last night, your husband would already be looking at you differently. Men can tell; they feel it right away.

At that moment, Valentina enters. Iris keeps quiet, though she doesn't disappear at once. She stands there, with her jewelry and her ironic smile, for a few moments.

VALENTINA: He's marvelous, darling. He's so enlightening. He's an initiate. He understands everything, he explains everything to you. Since I found him, I tell you . . . another . . . another life. It's dangerous—Bhisma, those séances. Very dangerous. Illusory. I was losing myself. He has enlightened me. I'm coming afloat again. He points out all my complexes. The secret is there: self-revelation. To know yourself. Now I know. My complex is one of self-destruction.

Juliet listens and does not hear. Her long-repressed anguish explodes. She bursts into tears, throws her arms around Valentina's neck; Valentina, too, begins to cry.

JULIET: Oh, Valentina, Valentina.
VALENTINA: Darling, dear. My sweetest.
JULIET: What's happening to me?
VALENTINA: Oh, my dearest Juliet.
JULIET: I slept on the floor all night. I can't even move. I'm mortified. Mortification. The humiliation. Should I sacrifice myself? Is that it? Or not? The pain. The suffering . . .

Valentina, who understands nothing and has absolutely no idea what to say, continues to hold her, crying.

VALENTINA: Oh, you poor darling.

JULIET: Yes, yes. That's it. That's it. That's what she was trying to tell me. With that look. You'll see that she'll come back. Oh, I'm going crazy; I don't understand anything any more.

VALENTINA: Dear, dear, dear. What an angel you are! You are such a beautiful soul. Oh, you poor thing.

JULIET: But why are you crying? You don't even know what happened to me, why I'm crying.

VALENTINA: It breaks my heart to see you like this. What did happen to you? No, don't tell me. It's too awful. Tell it to him. Should we speak to him about it? You have to tell him everything about yourself, your past—just like you told me so often, but even things that you haven't told me. Everything, everything.

They are interrupted by the repeated sound of a horn coming from the gate. Juliet looks outside and says, fixing herself up:

JULIET: My sister—Fanny.

She goes out, followed by Valentina.

THE GARDEN. EXTERIOR. DAYTIME.

Fanny, followed by two young men, is arriving, just as Juliet and Valentina enter the garden. Fanny goes up to her mother and kisses her; she kisses her sister, drinks something, offers something to the young men and is ready to leave.

FANNY: What is this? Oh, Scotch. Yes, we start rehearsals next week. Hi, Juliet, what's the matter? You're green. Know who I met? Mariella, with Arturo. Who did the dye job, Mother? You look marvelous. I've got to leave right away. Luigi will be waiting at Piazza del Popolo at half past seven. Hi, Valentina. Isn't Raniero here? Oh, yes. Hi, Raniero. Mother, look what this upswept hair style does for me. They say it makes me more photogenic.

The mother turns to Giorgio, who is gallantly kissing her hand.

MOTHER: Are you leaving, too?

Adele, full of insinuations, adds:

ADELE: Do you work even on Sundays?

Paying no attention to her tone of voice, politely, Giorgio says:

GIORGIO: Public relations. A group of Americans. We'll take them to dinner somewhere. Folklore. You're beautiful, Mother. You look like an empress. I'd court you. Good-bye, Juliet. Will you come with me to the gate?

He moves away slowly. The mother follows him with a look of affection and whispers to Juliet:

MOTHER: He's seven years older than you are, but you look like you could be his mother. He's getting bored, bored. Don't you notice? Poor thing. What a handsome man. Go on with him to the gate.

Juliet reaches Giorgio when he is almost at the gate. She looks at the long street that passes in front of their garden and then through the pines, passing other houses and gardens. Fanny's car is already leaving. Giorgio is getting into his.

STREET. EXTERIOR. DAYTIME.

In a deadened voice, Juliet asks:

JULIET: Will you be back late?

Giorgio starts the car; answers vaguely, without looking at Juliet:

GIORGIO: Oh, I don't know. (*He waves his hand from*

the window while the car pulls away quickly.) Good-bye!

Juliet remains alone at the gate.

In front of her the setting sun cuts through the tall forest pines.

Slowly, two lions emerge from the trees, advancing solemnly and meekly.

They precede a hermit, who stares at Juliet with eyes of fire. His voice seems a burst of thunder.

HERMIT: I am the lord of justice, and God has said that revenge is my privilege. Trouble to those who tolerate sin! Trouble! Whoever becomes an accomplice to the sinner will burn with him in eternal fire. You are righteousness offended, justice tread upon, faith violated. Claim justice and revenge in the presence of God.

Valentina and the young psychoanalyst are leaving by the gate. They walk slowly; Valentina is talking about Juliet.

VALENTINA: . . . and everything stems from her childhood. Poor darling. Don't you think so? That mirror . . .

Realizing that they are talking about her, Juliet joins them: she listens to the doctor apprehensively, looking at him closely to get his reactions.

The three walk on slowly.

VALENTINA: Tell him about the mirror. Yes, that you've always had a complex about mirrors. She was always looking at mirrors, poor thing. Even when she was a little girl. She even hid one under her pillow, and one night she saw the image of her mother dressed as a queen, with a crown and a cloak in it.

Hesitating, Juliet contradicts her.

JULIET: No, no.
VALENTINA: No? Of course, you told me about it your-

self. Seeing your mother dressed as an empress, with a crown on her head and with a cape.

JULIET: But not in a mirror. One night, in the hall. I got up. Maybe she was going to the theater.

VALENTINA: Poor darling, always something about her mother, her sisters. She always saw herself as the smallest. But you're not even ugly. Isn't it so that she isn't ugly? She has this complex . . . the mother . . . the sisters. Because her father—you tell him, dear. Or should I?

JULIET (*startled*): No, no. Forget it.

VALENTINA: But he has to be told, dear. You simply must tell him everything. This thing about your stepfather—I've always said so—is fundamental. Imagine! He was a Fascist. He used to tell her that Julius Caesar and Mussolini were the same person.

JULIET: No, no. It was I who got that idea. He always spoke of Il Duce. He was convinced—but this isn't important.

VALENTINA: Were you a Fascist, Doctor? My goodness, what goings on! Now tell him. If you don't, he can't possibly understand. He wasn't her father, you see? Oh, God, I get goose flesh just talking about it. She thought he was her father, but she was really someone else's daughter. Her mother, before marrying . . . But she found out everything later.

JULIET: When he died—from the notary.

PSYCHOANALYST: Did you ever know about your real father? (*Both women shake their heads.*) Well, this way it's impossible to tell. You'd have to start a whole series. It wouldn't be responsible for me to go on this way.

VALENTINA: You see, it's like Cinderella. Set apart, extraneous. Look, I have goose pimples. My, what a strong hand you have. So when the husband came along . . . Maybe even an incest complex, don't you think? The husband became everything to her. You're right that the fables are the fundamental archetypes. Cinderella, Little Red Riding Hood with the wolf . . . That explanation you gave the other day of Little Red Riding Hood really upset me. You can't imagine how I cried later on!

Juliet stops following the discussion. She stares at the thickness of the forest.

A flame is lit among the tree stumps; a flame that becomes a fire, and on it a grating, the grating of the saint. She is very young, very sweet, expressing both terrible suffering and superhuman joy. The eyes of the saint are fixed on Juliet's for a moment; then they turn to the sky.

Juliet suddenly looks rebellious, as if she wanted to reject totally, with all her being, this invitation to a resigned and joyful suffering.

She says forcefully:

JULIET: No! Not like that! It isn't fair.

LOBBY. RESIDENCE PALACE. INTERIOR. DAYTIME.

Juliet, at the concierge's desk, asks aggressively:

JULIET: Miss Olson. Gabriella Olson.
CONCIERGE: I don't know if she's in. Whom should I announce?

HALLWAY. RESIDENCE PALACE. INTERIOR. DAYTIME.

Juliet, preceded by a small, bouncing elevator boy, walks down the hall and stops in front of a door.

The elevator boy knocks and opens, letting Juliet in.

GABRIELLA'S ROOM. INTERIOR. DAYTIME.

Juliet enters, tense and hostile, and looks around.

There is no one in the room. It is like a drawing room, with an arched screen that separates it from the bedroom and bathroom. It is furnished with impersonal elegance, but Gabriella has put the stamp of her personality on it.

Some photographs of her, many very large, are hanging above the desk. There are flower vases with large, dry leaves, a few exotic memories of a rather pleasant disorder that remind one of the free life of the occupant. A large painting by Cy Twombly, many fashion and art magazines, a porcelain

Chinese horse, some Burmese fabrics, a very elegant black-and-white kimono thrown carelessly over an armchair.

The sound of footsteps and the feeling of a presence make Juliet turn around. Gabriella has come out of the bedroom. She is beautiful, very sure of herself, somewhat surly. She speaks with a slightly artificial but warm and sensual voice, with a marked courtesy. She is Swedish, so she speaks with a foreign accent and in a strange Italian, mixed with German and French words.

> GABRIELLA: I haven't had breakfast. Excuse me. (*She picks up the phone.*) This is room seventy-three. Would you send up the usual milk? Thank you. And a ham sandwich with just a little bread. (*She speaks to Juliet.*) Do you want anything?

Juliet shakes her head.

Gabriella puts the receiver down. Juliet hasn't stopped looking at her for a moment; and Gabriella, too, without being obvious, has continued to examine her rival. Finally, Gabriella says:

> GABRIELLA: So, you wanted to talk to me?

Juliet strains to find a way to start; her voice comes out oddly.

> JULIET: I didn't come for any revenge, nor to ask for anything. Just to speak to you. To get out of a situation that is painful to everyone—even to you, I imagine. But you have nothing to fear. I feel no hatred or anger toward anyone. And I'm not here to beg. But it doesn't seem to me worthy of you—of either of you—to act this way toward me. Considering me an enemy. That's it; that's why I came.

She stops speaking, filled with emotion.

Gabriella, who has been listening to her with a stony expression on her face, now raises an eyebrow.

GABRIELLA: I think you are the victim of an error—of false information—of a doubt. I know your husband. That is—it's been some time since I've seen him. Maybe two weeks, I don't know. But I have been seen with your husband, yes.

JULIET: Many times.

GABRIELLA: Yes? Maybe. Together with old friends, or even alone. We've gone to dinner together. I've accepted his company—friendly, discreet—with pleasure, also because this is my work, signora. To know people, to have friendly dealings. I am a woman who lives alone, and often I can't permit myself the luxury of turning down an invitation. I have to take solitude into account. But what you tell me—that would be something else. (*She is interrupted by the entrance of a waiter carrying a tray.*) Thank you. But why don't you knock?

WAITER: Didn't I knock? Yes, I did.

Gabriella has to pick up the conversation again; she makes an effort.

GABRIELLA: Do you understand? There's a great difference. (*She pauses.*) Why should I take a husband away from someone? It's not my style. (*She gets up and paces up and down the room, unsettled.*) Don't you think I'd have the courage to assume my responsibilities? They must have told you that we were seen together. I don't deny it. I don't deny anything. But it's normal nowadays. Your husband—(*She stops a moment, then continues with an effort.*) Your husband is nothing more to me than one of many companions, a friend. And look: It isn't because I don't like him. I want to be completely honest. (*Juliet nods her head, flattered.*) But I am a woman alone. I have my reputation, my interests. (*Confidentially.*) I can't afford the luxury of an "extra" relationship—(*she corrects herself*)—a steady one. You don't know the world I live in—the world of fashion. The hatreds, jealousies, pettiness. (*She starts pacing the room again.*) What should a woman do—shoot herself? Or else say: "Sorry, you have a wife, and we're not discussing business. We can't see each other, or we can only see each other in the company of others."

Juliet is confused. Gabriella's frank denial and the revelation of Gabriella—in addition to her obvious elegance—as a woman similar to Juliet, passionate and simple, is placing her in a comic situation. Nevertheless, she has the proof in her pocketbook. She opens it, takes out the agency's pictures, and puts them on the table, pushing them toward Gabriella.

Gabriella picks them up, looks at them silently, grimaces, and throws them contemptuously on the table.

GABRIELLA: How disgusting! Even spying! How awful! (*Juliet doesn't have the courage to tell her that she herself ordered the pictures taken.*) What a mean, miserable world! And they even send them to you! Poor woman, how awful for you. As soon as I can, I think I'll leave Rome. Far away, among the Zulus—among the cannibals. At least they have the courage—(*She stops, seeing that Juliet is upset.*) It's a horrible world. (*Suddenly she becomes the hostess—friendly, understanding, affectionate.*) Don't you really want anything? A whiskey? I'll get it for you. (*She goes quickly to a little bar and pours some whiskey into a glass.*) Soda? Unfortunately, I have no ice, but I can call downstairs.

JULIET: No, thank you. It's fine this way.

Gabriella brings her the glass; now that Juliet has her whiskey, Gabriella feels that she can begin to eat her sandwich. She does so elegantly, breaking it into little pieces, taking small, careless bites.

Juliet smiles at her. Suddenly her eyes fill with tears of joy and shame. Gabriella says very sweetly:

GABRIELLA: Signora. (*She gracefully gets on her knees before Juliet and takes her hand in a friendly gesture.*) I want you to believe me so badly.
JULIET (*moved*): I, too, would like . . . (*She pauses.*)

Should I say that I made a mistake? Is that what I should say?

Gabriella makes an evasive, condescending gesture.

GABRIELLA: Everyone makes mistakes nowadays. (*She signals to say it isn't necessary.*) A little more whiskey?
JULIET: No, thank you. I'd get drunk right away. (*She pauses.*) If you say I've made a mistake—if you swear it—(*She looks hopefully at Gabriella, hoping she will reassure her once and for all. Gabriella hesitates a little before nodding her head.*) Do you swear it?
GABRIELLA: Why not? If this will remove all doubts, why not?
JULIET: Then swear, please.
GABRIELLA: Of course I swear it. Yes.

Juliet impetuously tears all the photos into little pieces.

JULIET: Thank you. Forgive me. (*Drying a tear, she smiles nervously.*) I've wasted your afternoon.
GABRIELLA: You think so? It's been a necessary explanation, a useful one. I'm very glad you came. Now everything is clear. (*Juliet gets up, fixing her makeup*). Do you want to use the bathroom?

JULIET: No, no. I'm leaving. It's late. It's beautiful here, charming. You've fixed it so tastefully. And it must be comfortable, isn't it?
GABRIELLA: What can you expect these days, without servants? At least here it's like an apartment. I can invite anyone I like. (*She corrects herself.*) It's like a home without the trouble. And for the kind of life I lead—going here and there, never any security . . .

Gabriella opens the door. Juliet extends her hand. She would like to say something but can only mutter a "thank you." Gabriella smiles, and they exchange appropriate farewells. In the end, as Juliet goes out, she turns once more to smile at Gabriella, who waves from the doorway.

LOBBY OF RESIDENCE PALACE. INTERIOR. DAYTIME.

Juliet walks out of the elevator, crossing the lobby to head for the exit. Seeing the bar open, she goes in. She asks the bartender:

JULIET: A little mineral water, please. Thank you.

The bartender serves Juliet. In the meantime she takes a bottle of pills from her pocketbook. Obviously she has a headache. She is tired, emotionally exhausted.

She takes a pill, a swallow of water, leaves some change on the bar and is about to go out. Suddenly she stops: In the lobby she sees her husband.

He goes right to the elevator. He is obviously at home; he doesn't even ask the concierge anything. Maybe he has an apartment. Number seventy-two?

Juliet's eyes follow him dully. The elevator door closes; the elevator starts to ascend.

COUNTRY ROAD AND CAR. EXTERIOR. DAYTIME.

Juliet is driving, her eyes staring blankly ahead. She skids, rights the car at the last moment when other cars or trucks come close to her.

It is still afternoon, but the sky is full of clouds that threaten rain. The country street runs alongside a canal of still, dark water, on the outskirts of the airport.

From the back of the street comes a short funeral cortege. It is a farmer's funeral. In front of it, a motorized cart. Above it, a small coffin of light wood: It is the coffin of a child, covered with wild flowers. Behind the cart, a two-wheeled carriage, and on top of this the priest and a choirboy, who is carrying the cross. Behind them, on foot, a group of about a dozen people. In front of them, an old woman pushing a bicycle, on the handlebars of which sits a baby. Then other men and women, most of them old, all with bicycles in hand. Many also have umbrellas.

The cortege passes Juliet's car, which is stopped on the road. They look at it; it is empty.

Juliet is ten steps from the car. She has been looking at the canal but is now distracted by the passing of the funeral. She makes a quick sign of the cross. They all look at her. Serious faces. Women with black handkerchiefs, men with hats. The priest vaguely nods in greeting to Juliet. He evidently recognizes her.

When the cortege has passed, Juliet makes a motion of anger and grief. She throws away two or three flowers she had picked, walks farther from the car, and sits down on the embankment. She mechanically throws rocks in the water, not in anger, but almost to entertain herself. She turns around to look at the cortege, which is fading in the distance. More than saddened, she is troubled by the memory of something that suddenly comes to mind.

A funeral similar to this one . . .

A funeral that comes toward us . . .

A simple funeral cart, covered with wreaths. On one wreath is written: "To Laura; her schoolmates."

And right behind the cart, just after the relatives, a group of girls, Laura's schoolmates, among whom we recognize Juliet. They are all very sad, and some of them are crying.

A RIVER.

A wide river in the north of Italy. On the embankment a group of people around an ambulance; from the gravel bed comes a small group, four of whom carry a body wrapped in a blanket.

Among the group of people waiting on the embankment is Juliet. Around her voices are heard whispering.

> VOICES: Poor thing. . . . Such a beautiful girl. . . . A tragedy of love. . . . She's the daughter of the engineer of the Centrale. . . . So serious. . . .

THE EMBANKMENT AGAIN.

Juliet is still seated on the embankment. With great effort, she throws the last rock into the river; then she covers her face.

1. The séance. Giulietta Masina as Juliet.

2. Juliet's husband (Mario Pisu) in a marriage which has lost its savor.

3. Caterina Boratto plays Juliet's regal and domineering mother.

4. Two of the beautiful and sophisticated women who chide Juliet for her plainness and naiveté are her sister Sylva (Sylva Koscina, *left*) and her friend Valentina (Valentina Cortese).

5. With friends at the beach: her doctor (Felice Ful-
chignoni) and Lia Pistis.

6. The apparition of Iris (Sandra Milo, who also
plays the role of Susy and the circus ballerina).

7. Susy and her attendants at the beach.

8. Juliet's fantasy premonition of the detective (Alberto Plebani).

9. The terrifying image of death.

10. The Turkish invaders.

11. Landing of the Turkish barge.

12. The Sculptress: "God has the most beautiful body...."

13. Juliet with the sculptress' models (Nadir Moretti and Alba Rosa).

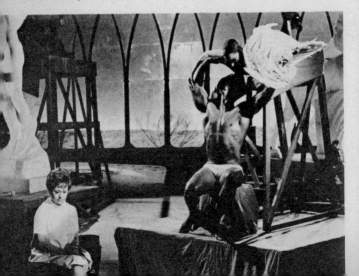

14. A visit to the Indian medium Bhisma with Valentina.

15. Middle-aged women who have come to Bhisma's suite.

16. Bhisma (Waleska Gert) and his assistants (Soujata and Asouka).

17. The apparition in Bhisma's suite.

18. An American painter is told to cut off Soujata's head.

19. Juliet as a child visits the circus with her grandfather (Lou Gilbert).

20. The grandfather and the circus ballerina as Iris.

21. Grand finale of the circus ballerina.

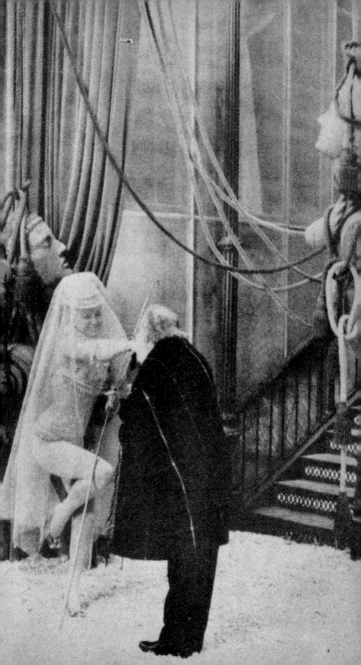

22. The escape of Juliet's grandfather and the ballerina in his aeroplane.

23. Juliet's mother and her children are left behind.

24. Linx Eyes, the detective.

25. The school pageant. The sisters prepare the children with angels' wings.

26. Juliet as a martyr in the school play.

27. Juliet's grandfather witnesses the performance.

28. Outraged, he disrupts the proceedings.

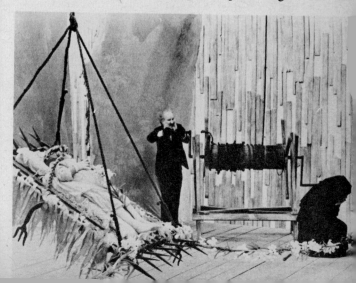

29. The visitor, José, who fulfills Juliet's romantic dreams.

30. Juliet's husband uses a telescope to spy on Susy in her bedroom.

31. A fantasy image: the barbarian horseman in the garden.

32. Susy grants the fetishist the right to keep her shoe.

33. Juliet and Susy in Susy's villa.

34. A wandering monk comes to admire Susy's beauty.

35. From Susy's bedside, a slide leads down to the pool.

36. At Susy's party.

37. Above Susy's bed, the vision of the child-martyr.

38. In Susy's bedroom with the Indian lover (Fred Williams).

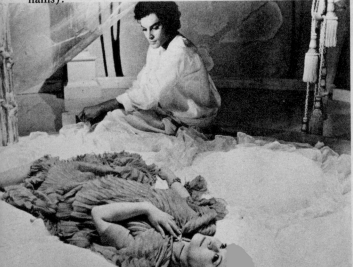

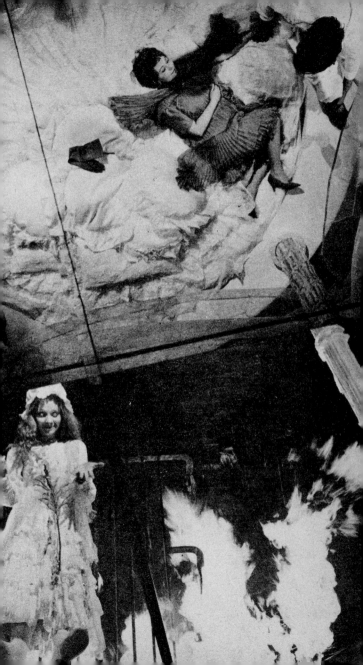

39. The garden party.

40. Valentina and the doctor at the psycho-drama.

41. Juliet's nieces at the party.

42. Eve and the serpent.

43. Separation.

44. Susy as an apparition.

45. A memory of the wedding day.

46. The phantasmagoria begins: José and the nuns.

47. Linx Eyes among the invaders.

48. An apparition of Juliet's mother.

50. *Over:* The apparitions depart.

49. Barbarians from the Turkish barge.

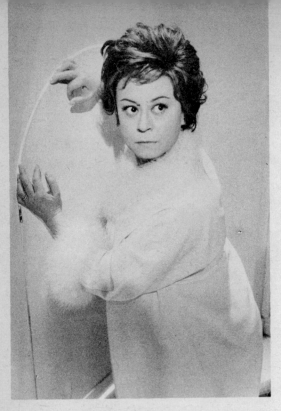

51. The secret door.

52. Release of the spirit-child.

JULIET'S VOICE: God, God! Like Laura? Must it end like that? To find You?

The funeral procession has passed completely from sight. Juliet is dejected, head in her hands. The sky has become darker; rain is imminent.

The roar of very distant thunder. Juliet, who is staring at the ground in front of her, is suddenly aware of something.

Two naked feet are next to her, two feet that are wet and dirty with grass and mud.

Raising her head, Juliet sees in front of her a pale girl whose clothes are splattered with water and mud. It is Laura. Her eyes, too are watery, filled with a superhuman sadness. Juliet instinctively pulls herself away, incapable of getting to her feet. She leans back to see Laura more distinctly.

Laura walks slowly, without looking at Juliet and without speaking. Juliet calls to her softly, anxiously:

JULIET: Laura, Laura. (*Laura looks at her; in her eyes there's no expression but that of mortal sadness.*) Laura!

Laura pulls her shoulders together. She says in a monotonous voice, in a tone that death seems to have fixed in her:

LAURA: Guido didn't come today. He is engaged to Ernesta. He doesn't want to see me any more. He doesn't want to see me ever. And I was his. What am I doing then in this world? It's just as well to die, to die.
JULIET: But, Laura, so many years have passed.
LAURA: I told him I couldn't live without him. I waited for him for three hours on the road. What do I do—go back home, back to school, like before? What is left in life? I'd just as soon die. (*She hunches her shoulders again.*) I don't know. Gray . . . fog . . . I'm alone.

She is moving away. Juliet tries to hold her back.

JULIET: Wait, Laura—but, God, God—haven't you seen God?
LAURA: Guido isn't there. I don't know. Gray. I'm alone.

I'm alone where I am.

Thunder. Large raindrops begin to fall, hiding the figure of Laura, who disappears along the canal.

JULIET'S HOME. EXTERIOR. EVENING.

Juliet's car stops in front of the gate.

Her hair is wet, her clothes soaked through. She is dead tired. A drowned woman.

From Susy's villa, the sounds of dance music from a phonograph. Susy is enjoying herself.

Juliet goes through the path that leads to the veranda and enters the house. She is disorganized. She throws her purse on the armchair, passes her hands over her face to dry herself. The cats are in the kitchen and in the garden. Upon seeing her, they come to life. They come toward her—miaowing, asking for love, food, attention.

Juliet pays no attention to the cats; she goes through the house, touches objects here and there, mechanically straightens a picture on the wall. Then she goes to the bedroom.

Her husband is there—like a thief. He has put a suitcase on the bed and is filling it with clothes from the drawers. Another suitcase, already closed, is on the floor.

Juliet stops at the doorway and looks at Giorgio. His back is to her, and he doesn't realize that she is there. But now he stops, as if he senses a presence. He turns and sees Juliet. There is a half smile on his face.

> GIORGIO: Oh, it's you. (*He points to the open suitcase as if to say that he's leaving.*) I'm getting ready. I have to leave. (*He sees that his wife is in a sorry condition, and he looks sorry.*) What did you do? The rain? Didn't you have the car?

Juliet nods her head.

> JULIET: Where are you going?
> GIORGIO: What? Just a trip. Two days. Milan. A nuisance.
> JULIET: With her?

GIORGIO (*shocked*): What?

JULIET (*not insisting on this point*): Will you stay for supper?

GIORGIO: Yes, if you think— Very little. I'm not hungry. I have a late train. If you think . . .

Juliet doesn't answer. She leaves the room and goes to the kitchen, where the cats have taken over and are impatiently waiting for her. She opens the refrigerator, hesitates a moment, then takes out a large piece of meat, which she throws to the cats, as if to say that they should hurry up and get on with it. All the cats throw themselves on the meat; two of them grab hold and one manages to escape, dragging the other behind him.

The cats flee, making eerie sounds.

Juliet sits on a kitchen chair and looks at the sink. She must do something, prepare the supper. With infinite weariness, she gets up, takes a pan.

AT SUPPER.

Juliet and Giorgio eat in silence.

Juliet hardly touches her food. Giorgio eats calmly, politely, as if he had been invited to supper by someone he hardly knew.

When he raises his eyes from the plate, he finds Juliet staring at him. Dumfounded, he smiles a little. He offers her a dish of food.

GIORGIO: Aren't you eating? Have some.

The television is on; a variety program with music and dance.

Juliet continues to stare at her husband, but without looking at him, as if his place were empty.

GIORGIO (*surprised*): What are you doing?

JULIET: Nothing. Just getting used to looking as if you weren't there.

GIORGIO (*disconcerted and cautious*): I don't understand.

Silence. Then Juliet cups her ear. She asks:

JULIET: Don't you hear the noise?
GIORGIO: What noise?
JULIET: A noise of someone digging under the house to get in. (*Silence.*) No, it's over.

Giorgio looks at her. His face is strained.

GIORGIO: You're tired. Have a little wine. (*Without any transition, as if to relieve himself of a great burden, he continues.*) I'm tired, too. I went to the doctor today. He says—he says—a cure, a period of rest would be good for me. A period of solitude.

On this last word, which he speaks awkwardly, he jumps to his feet and goes to turn off the sound of the television. On the screen images of silent singers and dancers remain, unreal. After a pause, Juliet says:

JULIET: So you will be away for two days. Maybe more?
GIORGIO: It would be good. I don't know exactly.
JULIET (*very calmly, making an effort*): Anyway, I know everything. I saw you at her place today. I even had a talk with her. Didn't she tell you?

Giorgio turns around; his eyes become hard and cold. He is obviously prepared for any explanation.

GIORGIO: All right. But it's not what you think.
JULIET: You've been seen together a few times, for business. And you're going away together.
GIORGIO (*pacing the room, then stopping*): All right. That's right. But it's not what you think. I have to be alone. This is important for me, and for you, too. A period of separation, that's what it is. I think a period of separation would do us good, would be useful for

both of us. It will give us a chance to reflect, to take many things into account.

JULIET (*still calm*): It's not a trip, then. It's a period of separation. Not a trip with a friend, but—

GIORGIO (*interrupting*): Temporary. What do you think, that I want to leave? No. Only for a short time . . . to be isolated . . . to clarify. Oh, it hurts me to tell you these things, but I have to, in order to end this thing. I can't stand it any longer.

JULIET: What?

GIORGIO: Everything. I'm going crazy, that's what. I'm going crazy. This life, coming and going, the work— you. I want to get to the bottom of this and find out what ties me to her. It's necessary, to resolve an unbearable situation, but there's nothing definite, nothing that can't be fixed.

JULIET: You can't leave her. Is that right?

GIORGIO: What are you saying? I—I—you know that I love you. We've always been fine together. I've done my job—and now you make me feel guilty. I ask you to understand me. I have to free myself, to be free awhile, to try to reach a conclusion. We can't stay here looking at each other like two enemies. Only this.

Juliet gets up and goes to look at the silent television screen, as if it were suddenly important. Then she says calmly, reflectively, as if speaking to the wall:

JULIET: She's beautiful, young, very elegant. She knows how to live. Then, too, she lies almost as well as you do. Perhaps better, because you at least blush when you tell a lie. If ever the two of you start lying to each other . . .

She stops. Giorgio watches her, then glances furtively at his watch. He is in a hurry to leave and seeks a less pathetic way to do so. Humbly and sweetly, he says:

GIORGIO: I only ask you to have—I don't know—understanding. You know how much affection I feel for

you, what tenderness. And if we have to leave each
other, I say—

JULIET (*interrupting*): I fought like a fool. I thought
she was like the others. I wanted to know, to find out.
No, with this one it's different. You need solitude. And
for me you've reached the point of affection and tenderness.

GIORGIO (*astounded*): But isn't that important?

JULIET: There's a wall, a wall. On one side, tenderness,
affection; on the other side, everything. I'm no longer
young, and I'm not beautiful. That's it. Monsters, ghosts
came to tell it to me. Susy, Iris, Olaf . . . Make yourself beautiful, be more of a whore—hair this way, makeup that way, move your rear when you walk, look
straight at men, laugh, clear your throat—just be a little
more of a whore. Like both of them. Burn them alive.
Have your nose fixed, lose weight, gain weight. . . .
What the hell! Everything is wrong. (*Juliet doesn't realize that, during this outburst, Giorgio has silently left
the room. She goes on after a pause.*) You're right. But
go now, or you'll be late.

She turns around and sees that Giorgio isn't there.

As if awakening from a dream, she runs to the bedroom.
The bedroom, too, is empty. Evidently Giorgio has left by
the kitchen door, taking his suitcases with him.

The kitchen door is open. The cats have returned and are
miaowing desperately.

Juliet runs toward the gate in time to see her husband's
car leave. She lets out a heartbroken cry, but the car doesn't
stop.

She remains a minute to look, then turns back to the house
and goes to the television set, turning on the sound.

A song. She turns it off completely.

She throws herself on the sofa and looks up at the ceiling.
But something distracts her.

The muffled noise of the underground tunnel grows around
her. It seems now to be under the floor, toward which
Juliet puts her ear.

She gets up slowly and takes a few steps. She watches

the floor as if tracing the noise. She goes to the window and looks out.

GARDEN AND PINE FOREST. EXTERIOR. DAYTIME. (SUNSET.)

All around the house and among the trees are the fires of the invaders. The savage warriors, on horse and on foot, run around madly, setting up their wooden and iron war machines.

JULIET'S HOME. INTERIOR. DAYTIME. (SUNSET.)

Juliet withdraws from the window. She looks around.

She goes slowly to the bedroom. There is general disorder. After choosing the things he wanted to take with him, Giorgio has left clothing, laundry, ties strewn all over.

Mechanically, slowly, Juliet puts things in order. For a moment she turns her face toward one of Giorgio's jackets, lightly smelling it.

His golden coffee cup is still on the little gas stove. His pipe is on a table. Juliet removes them and puts things in order with almost religious attention.

A sudden flash of light—passing like lightning across the windowpanes—attracts her attention.

She goes to the window. Lighted darts, thrown by the barbaric war machines, begin to fall in the garden. Juliet rushes to close the window, barring it. Then she pushes a piece of furniture against it. She moves on to the living room and calls out:

JULIET: Fortunata! (*No answer; she calls again.*) Fortunata!

A shadow passes quickly along the veranda: It is a bearded invading warrior.

Juliet runs to close the living-room window, too. The muffled noise is coming closer. The floor shakes. The glare of flashing darts, too, comes nearer.

She resolutely returns to the bedroom. She goes to the chest, opens a drawer, takes out two bottles of medicine and uncorks them, then pours all the pills into her hand. The water bottle is empty. She takes a glass and goes wildly to the bathroom.

She opens the bathroom door; she is petrified more from shock than from fear.

The bathroom is literally full of invading warriors. They are in the tub, on the bidet, in the basin of the toilet, in the sink. They are all eating something, and, unsurprised, they watch Juliet in silence.

Juliet quickly closes the door and runs to the kitchen.

The kitchen too, is full of invaders. Two are skinning a chicken; one is stirring a jar of honey with his finger, then licking the finger. Others are licking jars of marmalade and eating sugar. There must be twenty invaders, some even perched on the table and on the sink in a kind of silent bivouac. They move about, pass near Juliet without touching her. They stare at her with cruel eyes, but their movements are calm.

Juliet opens the pantry. Here they are packed closely like train riders in rush hour. Always the same looks of silent cruelty. Only their heavy breathing is heard.

The dining room is full of invaders. There are also women and children and a few horses. There is something grandiose about the bivouac, like an unreal, historic picture. However, the invaders have moved no furniture; they are simply making themselves comfortable, seated on whatever they find.

Juliet, making her way through the throng of bodies and armor with difficulty, reels toward the veranda. Her hope now is to escape through the pines.

She opens another door that should lead directly to the stairway. Instead, she finds herself in the large boudoir. In it is her dressing table. In the half light, the only form seen is that of her mother, abstract and marble-like, seated in front of the mirror. She is completely white—wearing a robe of very white silk; she is combing her hair with regal tranquillity.

With an almost childlike cry, Juliet stops at the door and leans toward her mother.

JULIET: Mamma, help me. Mamma. (*Smiling happily in*

the mirror, the mother continues to comb her hair, making no move to turn around. Her inhuman serenity is total and crushing, and Juliet speaks again, softly.)
Mamma.

She then turns and goes out of the room, carefully closing the door. She looks frantically for a real exit to the pine forest.

GARDEN AND PINES EXTERIOR. TWILIGHT.

Juliet, having climbed over and pushed aside the massive, heavy bodies, emerges, out of breath, in the garden. But a forest of multicolored flags seems to surround it from every side. Troops of barbarians on horseback are lined up all around, leaving no avenue of escape. The horses neigh and paw the ground. Threatening shouts come from all over.

Juliet feels lost. But suddenly something makes her look up: A wavering, multicolored light falls from above, right over her head.

It is a large balloon that is descending into the garden, a balloon with many large flags and festoons of lanterns of many colors.

In the vessel someone is signaling to Juliet—two people, a man and a woman, are leaning over the basket and waving. The man is Juliet's grandfather; the woman is beautiful and shapely in a chanteuse's dress—it is his famous adventure, the ballerina of the singing café.

Juliet lets out a desperate call, full of unexpected hope.

JULIET: Grandfather!

The grandfather continues to wave his arms, while the balloon continues its descent toward the garden. When it is but a few feet away, the grandfather throws a rope ladder overboard and signals Juliet to hurry.

GRANDFATHER: Come on. Quickly!

Juliet runs breathlessly toward the balloon, grabs the rope ladder and climbs it.

IN THE BALLOON.

Juliet is almost on board the little vessel. Two hands reach her, pull her; she falls in, head down, comically, complaining, very frightened, but at least safe.

The grandfather and the ballerina smile at her.

GRANDFATHER: How goes it, Juliet? You're a little pale. Get up. This way you'll be comfortable. Let me introduce you to Lia Belloni—on the stage, Ly D'Arcy. This is my granddaughter.

The ballerina extends her hand, both as introduction and in an effort to help Juliet up. She says in a sweet voice, lightly accented, bubbling:

BALLERINA: Oh, I'm pleased to meet you.
JULIET: The pleasure is mine. Thank you.

She gets up, helped by the ballerina. She clings tightly to the edge of the basket, still a little ill at ease, but smiling.

The large balloon is rising, and it heads over the pines; they begin to see houses and streets.

GRANDFATHER: This is the way to fly, I say. (*Juliet smiles in agreement.*) Simply—there's always wind. But look how we're moving. (*Juliet looks down, fascinated, instinctively looking for her own house among the plastic-like shapes already in the distance.*) Are you looking for your house? (*He bites off a cigar and lights it.*) Look, it's way down there. Right under my finger. And that little man there, that one there, in the little toy automobile, that's your husband. Or someone who could be your husband. They're all alike. How does that make you feel—ridiculous?

The ballerina laughs cordially, then says:

BALLERINA: Go on. All men are not alike. For example, you're different.
GRANDFATHER: Yes, I'm different, and so are you—and so is Juliet. The trouble is that the others are all the same. But, after all, to hell with them.

The ballerina laughs, and this time Juliet laughs, too. The ballerina offers her a heart-shaped box of chocolates.

BALLERINA: Signora, please take one.
JULIET: Thank you, but call me Juliet.

She takes a chocolate; so does her grandfather. They eat. The grandfather gives a big kiss to the ballerina. Then he sings.

Juliet laughs happily, filled with a sense of liberation, of well-being. She looks down: The town has become a spot among the trees. She sees the sea, the airport.

JULIET: Where are we going? Aren't we going back to earth?
GRANDFATHER: Relax. Relax. Of course, we're going back whenever you like. I've always returned. One always does return home, but the world is large—full of things to see and to do—above all, to do. (*So saying, he pats the thighs of the ballerina, who bursts out laughing.*) True, darling?

A bit obscenely, the grandfather winks at Juliet. Then, imitating an orchestra, he begins to sing, awkwardly and out of tune. With a great outburst, the ballerina, too, begins to sing.

Juliet laughs at first softly; then, carried away by the joy of the other two, she joins them in song.

While Juliet and the ballerina sing and skip together, already close companions, the balloon enters a cloud; everything becomes foggy. But the happy, impetuous song goes on.

RETURN HOME AND THE END.

Juliet's face is reflected in her bedroom mirror; she is still happily singing the old song. She stops singing, but, still laughing, she looks with surprise at her face in the mirror —as if she were seeing it for the first time.

She ruffles her ridiculous hairdo and energetically passes her comb through it.

She takes a paper handkerchief, soaks it in cream, and thoroughly cleans her face. She looks at the handkerchief, dirty with makeup.

She moves away from the mirror, puts on a wool sweater, and, looking at herself in the mirror again, dries off her face. She is still laughing, undoubtedly remembering the adventure in the balloon and her very frank and very kindly grandfather.

A voice, that of Fortunata, makes her turn around.

FORTUNATA: What, up already? Here's the newspaper.

Fortunata has just arrived; her apron isn't on, and she's wearing her overcoat with a handkerchief tied around her head.

JULIET: It's daytime, Fortunata.
FORTUNATA: Here's the newspaper. Will you have coffee in there? I'll put it on now.
JULIET: Thank you.

The sun enters from the open window. Everything is calm; outside, the usual sounds of a radio, a hen, a car.

These are the usual, comforting noises. There are no signs of the nocturnal siege.

Juliet takes the newspaper and puts it on the bed, without even looking at the front-page headlines.

She goes to the dining room. Everything is in order, except for the dining room table, which still has the remains of the supper—bottles and dirty dishes, a crude reminder of what has happened. A slight grimace, a small shrug of the shoulder, and she goes out into the garden.

Here, too, all is in order, with no trace of the siege.

The sun shining on the grass. An air of peace. The cats, as usual, sunning themselves.

The maid appears on the doorstep.

> FORTUNATA: The coffee is ready. What should I make for lunch today?
> JULIET (*without turning around*): I don't know—whatever you like.
> FORTUNATA: Will your husband be home for lunch?
> JULIET: No, I don't think so. Nor this evening.

Juliet goes to the swing, gently swinging, her feet not leaving the ground.

She continues to swing this way, absorbed.

She looks through the pines at the luminous horizon of the sea, colored in reds and golds, acquiring a magic beat, but supremely normal, everyday.

A sail, in the midst of the horizon, comes gently into the path of the sun. The sun is rising, reddening, the sail now lighted by a marvelously warm reflection, but marvelously "natural."

Juliet is quiet, almost serene, as she lightly swings. She looks around her at a world that more and more takes on—in ways so simple, so stable—both the real and the unreal pulse of everyday magic.

A flight of swallows passes high in the sky. Juliet raises her eyes and sees the swallows also slowly enter into the golden refraction of the sun's rays.

Juliet seems to be whispering something under her breath, but for the first time not in order to call or surprise anyone. She seems at peace with this pure world, filled with marvelous realities, which spring to life around her.

She hears a cry from above—it could be the sound of a group of birds, or the call of the swallows.

She raises her eyes, shields them from the powerful sun with the back of her hand. She tries to puzzle out the meaning of this faintly heard sound.

But she sees only the very blue sky—a blue as deep as a marine abyss—and the golden rays of the sun.

Juliet smiles, bends her head, and continues to sway on the swing, in the rustling of a light wind. It is as if she no longer cared about the origins of the sounds, the images she has seen, whether they be part of a natural mystery or part of a supernatural secret. Everything in her is now anchored in peaceful harmony, beyond the mystifying ghosts that have until now besieged her: she is concerned with the daily miracle of simple reality.

Juliet smiles, liberated, at peace.

AN ANGELO RIZZOLI PRESENTATION

OF

Giulietta Masina

IN

JULIET OF THE SPIRITS

CONCEIVED AND DIRECTED

BY

Federico Fellini

ORIGINAL STORY

Federico Fellini

Tullio Pinelli

SCREENPLAY

Federico Fellini

Tullio Pinelli

Brunello Rondi

WITH

Sandra Milo

Mario Pisu

Valentina Cortese   Waleska Gert

José de Villalonga   Fredrich Ledebur

Lou Gilbert

Caterina Boratto

Luisa della Noce   Milena Vucotic

Silvana Jachino   Fred Williams

Anne Francine

AND

Silva Koscina

SCENERY AND COSTUMES

Piero Gherardi

DIRECTOR OF PHOTOGRAPHY

Gianni di Venanzo (A.I.C.)

MUSIC

NINO ROTA

EDITING

Ruggero Mastroianni

A FEDERIZ FILM, SHOT IN THE STUDIOS OF
PALATINO AND CINECITTA. SOUND RECORDING
BY CINEFONICO PLATINO.

PRODUCER

Angelo Rizzoli

PRODUCTION MANAGER

Clemente Fracassi

DIRECTOR

Federico Fellini

PART THREE

TRANSCRIPTION AND TRANSLATION OF THE FINAL FILM

A weeping willow tree's bright green foliage brushes past as the camera moves forward. Night. The camera shoots up over one branch of heavy foliage and focuses on Juliet's home: a white picket fence, the lawn, the house—simple, painted white. Dark green shutters swung open against the outside of the house. The lights are on inside.

CUT

Hands holding flame to candles, close-up.

ELISABETTA
    Should I light the candles, signora?
TERESINA
    No. She said she'd light them.

Juliet calls in from another room:

JULIET
    Yes, I'll light them.

CUT

Juliet's dressing room. Nervous and excited, Juliet throws dresses and wigs out to her maids as she rejects them. She sits behind a partition that keeps her partially hidden.

TERESINA
    Oh, you're going to wear the red wig? I like the blond one much better.

JULIET

But, Teresina, I know what I should wear.

TERESINA

I'm sorry, signora, but I'm crazy about blond hair. What shoes are you going to wear?

JULIET

I've already got my shoes on.

TERESINA

I would have loved to give you a little something, but I sent all my money home.

JULIET

Don't worry—next time.

TERESINA

Oh, yes, this one fits you beautifully.

JULIET

What? It looks horrible. I won't wear any wig at all. I can't stand this dress. Take it.

She throws it out to her maids.

JULIET

And this thing here, too. Keep it, I'll give it to you.

TERESINA

Signora, did your husband tell you what he's going to give you? The present you bought for him is absolutely gorgeous. . . . Signora! Your husband is here. Hurry up! He's in the front yard.

Teresina takes the hat from Elisabetta.

Let me try that hat. . . . You know, signora, I'm so excited. How wonderful!

JULIET

Is everything ready out there?

CUT

Camera moves forward through a doorway into the dining room. The table, close-up, set for a festive but intimate dinner. We still do not see Juliet's face.

JULIET

Light the candles.

ELISABETTA

Your present is under his napkin.

TERESINA

One of your earrings is missing!

JULIET

I left it in the bathroom. Go get it, please.

Juliet lights the candles. The lights are turned out. Camera pans to the front door, then swings back and for the first time focuses on Juliet's face. She pats her hair and smiles nervously.

CUT

Giorgio, halts in surprise at front door.

GIORGIO

What's going on here? Aren't the lights working? What are you all doing there? . . . Oh, you're right, Juliet. What a beast I am! I'm terribly sorry. And I even wrote it down. . . . But I've got a surprise for you, too.

He calls outside.

GIORGIO

Ladies and gentlemen, welcome! It's our wedding anniversary! Juliet, look who's here.

Giorgio opens the doors. The camera shoots through the doors over his shoulder and moves outside. Giorgio's friends freeze along a path that crosses from door to gate. The camera photographs the entire group from the doorway. Valentina holds her tiny dog and a set of Japanese wind bells. Dolores's lover carries her in his arms. Juliet's lawyer, Genius, Elena, Raniero, Cesarino, and several others pose motionless along the path and among the small, decorative trees that border it. The freeze breaks, and the guests rush inside.

VALENTINA

Juliet, it's your wedding anniversary! Oh, dear. My love, look, I brought you a gift from Los Angeles.

She shows Juliet the wind bells.

GIORGIO
    Turn on the lights.
JULIET
    Thank you, but what is it?
VALENTINA
    It's to ward off the spirits. Hang it up.

Elena, a heavy woman of about 45, her face reinforced with heavy makeup and bright lipstick, kisses Juliet.

ELENA
    Hi, Juliet.

There is a babble of greetings. The guests take over the house.

GIORGIO
    It's been fifteen years, dear friends, fifteen years. . . .
VALENTINA
    Where's that dog gone? He's been so nervous for the last two or three days. . . .

She runs upstairs to look for the dog, pauses on the balcony at the top of the staircase, and shouts downstairs to Juliet.

    Oh, Juliet, I haven't introduced that gentleman to you. He's Genius, the greatest seer in the world.

Genius, dressed fantastically in a cape, tight pants, brilliant shirt, his face as heavily made up as Elena's, walks over to Juliet.

GENIUS
    My dear lady, I know everything about you. You were born under the sign of Aquarius, no? Many famous personages were born under this sign. . . .

Juliet's lawyer, fifty, portly, heavily jowled, kisses her hand.

LAWYER
    Ah, Juliet, it is always a joy to see you.

His greeting is exceptionally warm. The camera watches his

face, then pans around the room. We hear fragments of cocktail conversation. Giorgio comes up to Juliet.

GIORGIO

Why don't you get us something to eat?

JULIET

But what?

GIORGIO

Anything you want.

The camera swings to Cesarino, a neat, small, balding man. He points to Valentina and Raniero, who are squabbling, and says sarcastically:

CESARINO

They've made up!

RANIERO

Every time this idiot opens her mouth, I become blind with rage!

Camera swings to Dolores. She is about Elena's age and shows it, but she is less careful about her dress and makeup.

DOLORES

I'll cook, I'll cook! *Pilaf à la Dolores.* Do you have paprika, Juliet?

JULIET

Hot pepper.

DOLORES

All right.

JULIET

Let me help.

GUEST

Tell us what you're doing.

DOLORES

Ah, no. It's a secret recipe. To cook, to sculpt, to make love—these are my three passions!

ELENA (in the background)

I've been at a seance, too.

Dolores walks into the kitchen with her lover and Cesarino. The camera follows them. Dolores's lover is a handsome, well-built young man who wears his shirt open to the waist to exhibit his strong, hairy chest. He leans against the wall, bored.

CESARINO
Haven't I seen you at the gymnasium?
DOLORES'S LOVER
No, never.
CESARINO
I've done some weight-lifting, too.

Dolores opens the refrigerator.

DOLORES
Where's the tomato paste?

She goes to a cabinet.

Let's see here.

The cabinet is too high. She can't see into it.

Pick me up.

Dolores's lover picks her up. As he lifts her, when her face is just above his, she twists toward him and kisses him hungrily, slowly, deeply. When she reluctantly releases his lips, the camera breaks from her and pans back to the party in the other room. Elena walks over to Giorgio.

ELENA
What's this handsome fellow got to say to me?
GIORGIO
I don't need to say anything to you.
ELENA
Oh, but you're so mysterious. Not even at my age. . . .

Her words are lost in the babble of the party.

CUT

Juliet's dressing room. She talks with her maids.

ELISABETTA

    Do we have to feed all these people?

JULIET

    Of course—they're guests, aren't they?

The maids leave, and Juliet turns to look in a mirror. We hear the lawyer's voice.

LAWYER

    Where is Signora Juliet? May I come in?

Juliet looks at herself in the mirror and speaks to the reflection.

JULIET

    No, don't be stupid. Don't start crying now.

The lawyer opens the door of the dressing room.

LAWYER

    Juliet, tonight you look like a little doll. I have so many things I could say to you.

JULIET

    Please, excuse me. Patience!

She closes the door in the lawyer's face, just as Genius approaches the lawyer.

GENIUS

    Honorable Mr. Attorney, your sister's dreams can be explained very easily: the Indians believe in everything, like the Egyptians, the Etruscans; and the Chinese have lovers. . . .

Valentina draws Genius away toward Juliet's dressing room.

GENIUS

    Wait. . . .

VALENTINA
    Oh, yes, because the other night I dreamed. . . .

She takes Genius into the dressing room, excluding the lawyer.

    Excuse me, Attorney. . . .

CUT

Inside the dressing room.

JULIET
    But no, this is not the right moment. . . .
VALENTINA
    Come on—no, no, no. He said that at the first meeting
    he should try the pendulum.

Juliet sits before her mirror. Genius holds a small weight
on a string over Juliet's head. As he concentrates on its
motion, he shrugs off his cape.

GENIUS
    Valentina, put this down, will you?
VALENTINA
    Yes, maestro.
GENIUS
    Oh, I see beautiful things—there is a strong magnetic
    force.

Valentina hangs up the cape.

VALENTINA
    How strange this house is. Who lived here before?
GENIUS
    Let your mind go blank. . . . The reaction of the
    pendulum is positive. You see? It is swinging from left
    to right.

There is a knock at the door.

VALENTINA

Who is it?

Giorgio speaks outside the door.

GIORGIO

It's me.

He starts to enter.

VALENTINA

You can't come in.

GIORGIO

What are you doing?

VALENTINA

Nothing.

GIORGIO

I know: you're talking about me, aren't you?

Giorgio enters, and Valentina and Genius leave.

GIORGIO

I'm sorry to have brought all these people without
telling you, but, you see, they stopped by the office,
and I couldn't avoid inviting them.

JULIET

Oh, it's all right. You did the right thing. They're nice
people.

Giorgio turns to leave, but Juliet stops him as she rises from
the mirror.

JULIET

Giorgio . . .

GIORGIO

Yes?

JULIET

Do you love me?

Giorgio smiles. He embraces Juliet, lifts her up and swings
her around and around gently, dancing her back into the
party. The camera pans to follow them. The guests applaud
and offer congratulations.

GUESTS
     Good luck, good luck! Long live the happy couple. . . .

The lawyer congratulates them. As he bends to kiss Juliet's
hand, Giorgio, still dancing with Juliet, reaches down and
pats the lawyer's balding pate. In the foreground the camera
catches Elena and Cesarino.

ELENA
     Are you married?
CESARINO
     Would I say, "Long live the bride and groom," if I
     were married?

The camera watches Elena and Cesarino.

CUT

Valentina whispers to Genius.

CUT

Outside on the lawn, later. Giorgio and Cesarino stroll along
the path.

GIORGIO
     Ah, no. It is much better to lie.
CESARINO
     Ah, then you deserve a gold medal. Does your wife
     know that this is a hero's house?

He and Giorgio laugh.

CUT

Inside. The lights have been turned off again. The camera
cuts directly from outside to a quick shot of the two maids
in the kitchen, where the lights are still on. The maids are
seen through the frame of the kitchen-dining room pass-
through window. They are looking out into the darkened

living room, where Valentina is preparing the guests for the
seance.

VALENTINA

Sit around the table without crossing your legs. Meanwhile I'll purify the atmosphere.

The camera follows Valentina, who carries a lighted incense
stick through the room. She notices Raniero on a sofa, petting
a cat, and goes over to him.

RANIERO, drunkenly:

Pretty kitty. . . .

VALENTINA

Oh, no, not cats! They bring restless spirits.

RANIERO

Go on! Take your seance and . . .

Valentina continues her purifications. The camera follows
her for a moment, then swings back to the previous shot of
the maids. We hear Juliet's voice.

JULIET

You may go to bed now. Good night.

MAIDS

Good night, signora.

The maids climb the stairs. When they reach the balcony,
they pause to look down at the group below. The camera
pans upward to follow them.

ELISABETTA

I don't like it when she does these things. I'm scared.

TERESINA

Be quiet!

We hear Juliet's voice from below.

JULIET

Go on.

MAIDS
   Good night.

CUT

Camera, assuming the maids' viewpoint, looks down from
the balcony, at the group below. The living room is dark.
Juliet, Valentina, Dolores, and Elena sit holding hands
around a small, circular table. Incense burns on the table.
Raniero and Dolores's lover slouch on nearby sofas. Each
holds a cat. As the camera watches them, we hear Valentina's
voice.

VALENTINA
   God, how many spirits! They're all around.

CUT

A table-level 5-shot of the group. Camera draws in closer
to Juliet. She sneezes.

JULIET
   Excuse me. It's the incense.
GENIUS
   Concentrate.
VALENTINA
   There's a new spirit—someone never come before, some-
   one who wants to communicate with us.

CUT

Raniero and Dolores's lover on sofas. Dolores's lover holds
up an empty whiskey bottle.

DOLORES'S LOVER
   Ask your spirits to fill up the bottle. It's empty.

Camera swings back to the group at the table and draws
in for a close-up of Juliet. We hear Giorgio's voice.

GIORGIO

   . . . One . . . lengthen your step . . . two . . .

CUT

Just outside the windows along the front wall of the house, Giorgio and Cesarino play an exercise game. They take long, high, slow steps—almost a slapstick exaggeration of a goose-step—and chant in rhythm to their steps.

GIORGIO

   Longer . . . longer . . . One . . . two . . . Longer . . .

CUT

The hands on the table at seance, close-up. There is a sharp rapping sound.

GENIUS

   Here it is.

The camera moves from face to face around the table. Juliet looks around the table. All the others are concentrating.

VALENTINA

   Question him, maestro.

GENIUS

   Will you tell us your name?

Several raps.

GENIUS

   He said I . . .

Raps.

   . . . R . . .

VALENTINA

   Didn't he say "H?"

GENIUS
  Shhhh. He said R . . . I . . . S. Iris—a woman.
VALENTINA
  Iris! What a beautiful name. Who knows who she was?

CUT

The lawyer rises from a chair in the nearby shadows. Astonished, interested, he steps closer to watch. Juliet is concentrating. Delighted with the progress of the seance, and excited, she begins to participate wholeheartedly.

JULIET
  Could you say who you are?

Raps.

JULIET
  She said she is beautiful, didn't she, maestro?
GENIUS
  Yes, she said she is very beautiful.
VALENTINA
  Iris, listen: do you have a message for us?

Raps.

GENIUS
  She said, "Love for everyone."

Delighted, the women repeat the message. The lawyer, watching nearby, catches Juliet's eye and, holding her attention, bends slightly and slowly kisses the back of his hand. She turns her eyes quickly back to the table, shakes her head, "No," and flicks her shoulder in a gesture of annoyance.

VALENTINA
  Your message is very lovely. Listen, Iris, would you tell us . . .

A harsh noise interrupts Valentina.

VALENTINA

What's this?

GENIUS

Perhaps it's interference. Is it still you, Iris?

One rap.

She said no. Now, let's listen.

VALENTINA

What's your name?

Raps.

GENIUS

Olaf. He said his name is Olaf.

VALENTINA

Olaf. . . . Are you a Turk?

Raps.

GENIUS

He said that you'd be the Turk.*

VALENTINA

Oh! . . . Why don't you give a message to one of us? Something nice, something that could help us in our lives. What could you tell our friend Dolly?

Raps.

GENIUS

Whore. He said, "Whore."

VALENTINA

But no, dear, you don't understand . . .

Vehement rapping.

---

* In Italian; *troia* (Turk) also means whore.

GENIUS
Dirty whore. He said, "Dirty whore!"

Elena laughs loudly.

DOLORES
Thanks. That's not an insult, you know.
ELENA, still laughing:
He said, "Dirty whore!"

This sends her into another fit of laughter.

VALENTINA
Poor spirit. Go in peace. Go in peace.

Close-up of Juliet. Though the others laugh, she is upset
by the coarse tone the seance has taken. She lowers her eyes
to the table. The phone rings. Juliet turns her head and
stares at the telephone.

CUT

Dolores's lover, on the sofa, picks up the phone. We hear
Valentina's voice.

VALENTINA
Won't it send them away?
DOLORES'S LOVER
Hello? Hello! Who is it? Bah! They hung up.

Raps.

GENIUS
Ah, Juliet, we have a message for you: "Who do you
think you are? You're no one to anybody. You don't
count, you wretched thing."

Knocks continue, but Juliet stands up, shocked by the message.

GENIUS
Hold on—don't break the chain. It's dangerous.

Juliet falls back into her chair, fainting. Her head rests on the table.

VALENTINA
Juliet! Giorgio!

The chain breaks, and the guests gather around Juliet, babbling exclamations and advice. Giorgio comes in from outside.

GIORGIO
Who's sick? Juliet! Turn on the lights.

Genius is still in something like a trance. He talks to no one in particular.

GENIUS
. . . A girl, naturally . . . very gifted . . .

From Juliet's viewpoint, the camera pans up at the guests standing over her. Some smile, some watch curiously, some are disinterested. There is no sense of warmth or sympathy. The camera holds on Giorgio. Juliet throws herself into his arms.

JULIET
Giorgio!
GIORGIO
Juliet.

Genius walks away from the table, talking to himself.

GENIUS
Oh, yes, this girl is very gifted. Very, very gifted. . . .

CUT

Juliet's house, the next morning. Juliet asleep in bed. Giorgio's side of the bed is empty. We hear the sound of a car driving away. Juliet sits up.

JULIET
    Elisabetta!
ELISABETTA from an adjoining room:
    Yes, signora?
JULIET
    Has my husband left?
ELISABETTA
    Yes. He just left. He said that he didn't want to wake you, because you were up late last night. He said that he won't be back for lunch. . . . Your nieces are already at the beach with their nurse.

Juliet walks to the windows, lights a cigarette, sits on the window sill. It is a lovely morning. She smiles. Below, the gardener works in a small pool adjoining the house. Leaves and vines draped around him, his clothes clinging wetly to his huge, fat body, he climbs out of the pool like some creature from beneath the sea.

GARDENER
    Good morning, signora.
JULIET
    Good morning.
GARDENER
    I'm cleaning out the pool. These terrible leaves always clog the drain.
JULIET
    Very good, Gasperino.
GARDENER
    Beautiful day, isn't it?

He begins to sing, loudly and cheerfully.

GARDENER
    I'll fly, I'll fly to the arms of my beautiful love. . . .

The gardener walks off around the corner of the house. Juliet notices Teresina leaning over the fence in an embrace with a man.

JULIET
    Teresina!

Teresina breaks off and walks nonchalantly toward the house.

TERESINA
    Yes, signora? . . . Since the plumber was here . . .
JULIET
    A fine excuse!
TERESINA
    He's from my home town.
JULIET
    All right.

Clearly annoyed, Juliet walks into her dressing room. She sits down in front of her dressing table and looks at herself in the mirror. She whispers to herself.

JULIET
    . . . for everybody; love for everybody. . . .

She smiles, gets up, and measures her height on the bathroom scale. We hear the voice of Elisabetta.

ELISABETTA
    Should I set up the table outside, signora?
JULIET
    Yes, please.

CUT

The lawn, seen through the living room doors. Elisabetta carries a small table across the lawn and sets it up under a tree just outside the door. Above it hang Valentina's Japanese wind bells. The camera draws in toward the table. It is the same one used for the seance.

ELISABETTA
    Good morning, signora. I'll have the table set in a moment.

Juliet nods absently. She walks to the table, biting her lip
with timid anticipation and pleasure, remembering last night.
As she touches the surface of the table, it gives a sharp
rap. She lifts her hand, startled. The wind blows.

JULIET
    Is that you, Iris?

Raps. Juliet strokes the table top affectionately, smiling. The
wind blows suddenly, rattling the Japanese wind bells.

CUT

A brightly colored beach ball rolls along sand, chased by two
young girls.

CUT

Juliet's doctor's face close up—fat, healthy, suntanned, smiling broadly.

DOCTOR
    Haven't you ever been in a plane, signora? Haven't you
    heard the radio up there? You should hear those voices
    —giving orders, counterorders—human voices, ugly
    voices hoarse with phlegm. These are the voices of the
    air—not spirits, not spirits. My beautiful lady, when I
    hear such naïve talk, my scientific mind is offended.
    These are only electrical forces, whims of unknown
    substances. . . .
DOCTOR'S WIFE
    Couldn't they be communications from other planets,
    received by the unconscious mind?
DOCTOR
    Quiet!
DOCTOR'S WIFE
    Let me talk. I was saying, perhaps . . .
DOCTOR
    Be quiet! [He continues his lecture to Juliet.] In

any case, as your doctor I advise you not to continue
with these experiments.

As the doctor speaks, the camera draws back to show Juliet
and her friends at the beach, sitting on beach chairs under
a simple canopy: the doctor, always smiling; his wife, her
face puckered by wrinkles; Juliet; a manicurist who works on
Juliet's nails; Juliet's two nieces, pretty girls about three or
four years old; their nurse; and another woman, plump,
tanned, smiling, like the doctor. Juliet wears a completely
white outfit—a large sun hat with a huge brim, beach coat,
pedal pushers. As the friends converse, the camera shifts
from face to face, watching them.

JULIET
    But, Doctor, when I was a child, all I had to do was
    close my eyes and I would see . . .

The plump woman interrupts her.

WOMAN
    When I was a child, if I closed my eyes, I'd see balls—
    how many balls! And how beautifully colored they
    were!

DOCTOR
    Really? How nice.
JULIET
    . . . castles, piazzas at night, forests, tiny faces that
    would stare at me with huge, shining eyes. They fright-
    ened me, but it all was very beautiful. They continued
    for years, and then, suddenly, they stopped. . . . But it
    was enough just to shut my eyes. . . .

Juliet closes her eyes.

CUT

A beautiful young woman in a circus swing hangs in the
sky above the beach and sea. She smiles a huge smile behind

her filmy white veil. A short, low-cut trapeze artist's costume exhibits her full-bosomed, healthy body. Flowers have been twined around the ropes of the swing. The image holds very briefly.

CUT

Juliet's astonished face.

CUT

The doctor laughs uproariously. Next to him, the plump woman cheerfully masticates a snack.

DOCTOR
> That could simply be bad digestion. Once we are dead, we are but a handful of dust, and if some small bone does remain, we'd better watch out for the dogs. Go swimming, buy yourself a horse and take it jumping, but, above all, tell your husband to make love to you more often. Ahhhh—against the spirits and against toothaches, there is no better remedy than making love.

Juliet is somewhat embarrassed, but she smiles agreeably.

JULIET
> Oh, yes, I know, Doctor.

Suddenly she looks puzzled.

CUT

A canopied raft, pulled by a small, flat-bottomed boat, approaches the beach. The raft and the boat are filled with an amazing variety of exotic characters—colorful, beautiful, fascinating. A lovely young Eurasian woman stands at the prow of the boat. Susy reclines on pillows on the barge. As the boat runs ashore, two Oriental boys jump out and begin rolling two huge, thin-spoked wooden wheels up the beach. Other men pull the boat ashore.

CUT

The doctor stands up, amazed.

DOCTOR
> This is a real apparition! Oh, let me tell you, I believe in this apparition.

DOCTOR'S WIFE
> Don Raffaele, stop it, please.

DOCTOR
> This kind of apparition I'd like to have at night!

JULIET
> She is a neighbor, but—to tell the truth—we don't associate with her.

CUT

Susy's party parades down the beach. A liveried chauffeur and three other men carry a huge bed shaded by a brightly colored, Oriental canopy. On the bed there are baskets of food and fruit. The boys roll their wheels. Susy walks behind with several other women.

CUT

The doctor is fascinated.

DOCTOR
> Eh, Signora Juliet won't associate with her—but I would!

CUT

Susy's party sets up its pavilion near Juliet's group. Seen this close, Susy looks very much like the woman on the circus swing. She wears a tiny bikini that shows off her beautiful body, visible through a thin net veil that hangs from her bright yellow hat to her thighs.

CUT

Juliet purses her lips.

JULIET
    Mademoiselle, please bring the little girls back.

CUT

The children have run over to Susy's pavilion, where they
are now chattering with Susy. Their nurse, who wears an
ordinary white T-shirt over her awkward, shapeless body,
waddles over. Gracefully, Susy bends down and hands each
child a bunch of grapes.

NURSE
    Rosella, Caterina, say, "Thank you, thank you very much,
    signora."
CHILDREN
    Good-bye.

The nurse brusquely hurries the children away. Susy waves
cheerfully.

CUT

The camera compares the two groups, Juliet's and Susy's,
and then moves in for a close-up of Juliet. She looks into
a hand-mirror.

NURSE
    I'm going in for a swim, signora.
DOCTOR
    Our lovely Juliet always sees obscure, magical things,
    everywhere.

CUT

Susy sits on a stool by the water's edge, silhouetted against
the sea and the sky.

CUT

Juliet's group. The nurse tells the children a story in French. The camera moves in close on Juliet. She is falling asleep. As her chin drops toward her chest, her broad white hat covers the screen.

CUT

The sea—dark, dead calm, sinister. Slowly, a plump, old man walks up the beach from the water, pulling on a heavy rope that is slung over his shoulder. He wears a red bathrobe, a black hat, and spectacles. As he pulls, Juliet approaches him. The sound of wind. His voice is a loud, slow whisper.

MAN WITH ROPE
Juliet, will you help me please? I'm old, and besides, this really is your concern.

He hands the rope to Juliet, who begins to pull on it.

CUT

The sea and sky—dark green, ominous. Silence. At the left edge of the screen, slowly, the black silhouette of a ship's prow appears. From behind it, slowly, a raft floats into view. Two emaciated, exhausted horses, ribs showing, stand with their heads hanging to the raft's floor. Another horse lies on its back, motionless. It's legs, bent at the knees stick up into the air; its neck arches upward; its head twists painfully off to the side, like a figure from *Guernica*. Wind blows audibly.

CUT

Like a landing barge, the large ship drops its prow onto the beach. Inside the barge an eerie light reveals a bizarre, motionless tableau—naked or nearly naked men, one emaciated, bony, another fat and flabby; women naked or nearly naked. The nudity is disgusting, rather than appealing. They sit staring sightlessly, as if drugged. One man holds a sword, but there is nothing strong or violent about the group. All the figures seem afflicted by an unknown malady, exhausted. In the rear of the group stands a man in a white summer suit, staring straight at the camera. The camera cuts back and forth between the frozen tableau and Juliet's frightened face. We hear Juliet whisper.

JULIET
    Doctor, help me!

CUT

The doctor sits in a chair at a distance down the beach. He makes no motion except to turn his head slowly, as if looking from side to side, or saying, "No."

CUT

Inside the landing barge. Camera leaves the group and pans downward. Someone swims slowly around the prow, underwater. Another man lies on the beach near the ramp. Slowly, as if in a pointless ritual, he swings a sword toward the swimmer.

CUT

Juliet tries to run away, her back to the camera. Her feet sink into the soft sand. It slows her. It holds her back. She lifts each foot slowly, laboriously, in an exaggeration of the slowness and difficulty of running in sand. She moves no more rapidly than if it were a slow-motion sequence, but there is no smoothness. Juliet moves awkwardly, heavily.

CUT

About twenty yards out, another raft floats slowly past the beach. Many naked or nearly naked men sit on it. The emaciated man from the landing barge, standing at the front of the raft, holds a sword over his head as if he had drawn it upward before delivering a blow, or as if it were bearing a flag. A high-pitched, ear-piercing whine grows louder and louder. Out of the sea between the raft and the beach, the huge, bald head of a strong man appears. He begins to rise out of the water. He holds a club threateningly over his head. The shrill whine mounts to deafening intensity, and suddenly we recognize it as the scream of a low-flying jet plane passing overhead.

CUT

Juliet awakens, her face showing fear. The camera pans across the beach: The children play cheerfully with their nurse, sitting on the sand; swimmers pause peacefully at the water's edge. The camera swings back to show Lola, one of the women from Susy's entourage, walking away from Juliet's group. The doctor's wife holds up a basket of fruit.

DOCTOR'S WIFE
Juliet, that lady just sent us this lovely basket of fruit as a gift. Isn't she kind, though?

CUT

Susy stands beside her pavilion. She waves to Juliet, who nods a dignified thank-you and offers a slight, tight smile, which disappears as Susy drops her cape, raises her arms to the sky, stretches her full, beautiful body, and runs into the sea.

CUT

The pine woods. Juliet follows the children and their nurse through the trees. She smiles happily as she watches the children, but when she hears a bird's call, she pauses and looks around her, perplexed.

NURSE
Did you say something, madame?
JULIET
No, I didn't say anything. Children, don't run. Come here.

The children run ahead.

CHILDREN
   Mamma! Mamma!

Adele walks toward them through the trees. She is very pregnant; yet this does not seem to detract from her remarkable air of cool self-confidence and poise. Instead, it seems to add to it. She stoops to embrace the children. Juliet quickly checks her clothes.

CHILD
   Mommy, this morning on the beach there was a fish without its head! Brrrrrrr!

ADELE
   Did you go swimming?

Sylva appears a short distance behind Adele. One child runs to her.

CHILD
   Aunty, Aunty! This morning on the beach there was a fish without its head! Brrrrrrr!

SYLVA
   Stop! Don't touch me—you have dirty hands, dear. Hi, Juliet! . . . God knows, I'd like to have a little house here, too.

Adele carries one of the children.

ADELE
   But you are white! Mademoiselle, the little girl is absolutely white. You don't let her sunbathe. Don't you remember what the doctor said? She has to sunbathe at least two hours every day.

Sylva flounces through the trees toward Juliet, her full breasts bouncing in her low-cut dress. She recites in French and improvises a theatrical role.

JULIET
    Hello, Sylva. What a lovely surprise!
SYLVA
    Adele was coming to pick up the girls, and we thought
    we'd come with her. Here's Mother.

Juliet's mother joins the group.

JULIET
    Hello, Mother.

The camera focuses on Adele, Sylva, Juliet, and their
mother. Juliet's sisters and her mother are taller than she.
Even more than Adele, the mother is elegant, cool, proud,
self-confident, and rather aloof. Sylva also is self-confident
and elegant, but she is also very sexy, frivolous, and gay.
Next to her mother and sisters, Juliet seems to lose her com-
posure. She becomes quiet and apologetic. Compared to the
clothes her family is wearing, Juliet's seem simple and plain.
Her mother and sisters are artfully made up, whereas Juliet
uses no artificial aids.

MOTHER
    Have you been walking in the pine woods in this hot
    weather?
JULIET
    We were going back home. Besides, it's not too hot.
MOTHER
    Please. You are all sweaty.
JULIET
    Will you stay for lunch?
SYLVA
    Oh, no, I can't. I've got to be at the TV studio for re-
    hearsals at three o'clock.
ADELE
    It's two already—we're late. When do we have to be at
    Luciana's?
MOTHER
    At four. And then we have to go to the dressmaker's.

ADELE

Did the children bother you?

JULIET

Oh, no. They kept me company. They enjoy themselves
with me. . . . How pretty you are, Sylva.

SYLVA

Do you think so?

JULIET

Oh, yes.

SYLVA

I lost four pounds. My director wants me to be slimmer.
But how beautiful it is here! Do you enjoy your evenings here?

JULIET

Well, you know, actually there isn't much to do here at
night. Most of the time Giorgio is tired, so we'd rather
stay home.

SYLVA

By the way, what a fellow your husband is! The other
day he called me up and asked me if he could take me
out and show me off. He said some industrialists were
arriving from Brazil. I said, "Sure, I'll come with my
boy friend," and he said, "Oh, well, never mind. Next
time." *Oui,* I was annoyed!

ADELE

But isn't your husband ever here?

JULIET

Of course. He returns in the evenings. You know, with
his work . . .

ADELE, ironically:

Oh, the poor fellow—how he works! Does he get overtired?

JULIET

Yes, but he said that he'll take a vacation soon, and
we're going to go on a cruise together. Spain, Greece—
we haven't decided yet. But I have all the brochures already. This time we'll really go.

They have reached the cars, and the mother, Adele, and
the children begin to climb in.

JULIET

Good-bye, Mother.

MOTHER

Good-bye, love.

(To Sylva)

Good-bye, sweet.

CHILDREN

Good-bye, Aunt.

Sylva exchanges farewells with her mother and sister. With bright, quick movement the women lean to kiss each other, but they never touch. They kiss only a veil, or the air close to the other's face. Sylva flounces over to her Volkswagen, twirling her parasol.

SYLVA

Remember to turn on the TV set Saturday night. You'll see your little sister. I have a beautiful role. Good-bye.

JULIET

Good-bye, Sylva.

ADELE

See you Sunday, then.

Sylva drives off, and the camera draws back to watch Juliet saying good-bye. Everyone is already in the car—an expensive, chauffeured Citroen.

JULIET

Good-bye, Mother. . . . What is it?

MOTHER

I was just looking at you. Why don't you put on a little makeup and lipstick?

JULIET

You're right, Mother. But you see, we've been at the beach.

MOTHER

You must take better care of yourself. Good-bye.

CUT

The TV set in Juliet's living room, close-up. A pretty actress

demonstrates and explains some eye exercises. Juliet and
the maids watch together.

TV

. . . and exercise the eyes horizontally for ten minutes. . . .

Elisabetta laughs.

ELISABETTA

Signora, do you see how Teresina does it?

JULIET

No, you shouldn't move your head. Only your eyes.
Wait a second. Like this.

She demonstrates.

TV

. . . more and more rapidly. These exercises will give
back to your eyes the splendor . . .

CUT

Juliet and the maids as seen from outside the front door.
Giorgio walks into the house, his back to the camera.

GIORGIO

Good evening.

MAIDS

Good evening.

JULIET

Hi. Elisabetta, get the supper ready on a tray, here near
the TV set.

She walks over to Giorgio.

GIORGIO

No, dear, I'm not hungry. What a day I had! What's
on TV?

JULIET

Don't you even want a small piece of cake?

GIORGIO
    No, no. I had a snack at the office.
JULIET
    Sit here for a while.

She pats the seat next to her in front of the TV. Giorgio sits down wearily. He leans his head back and presses his sinuses with his fingers.

TV
    . . . in a melodious voice, you should speak the follow-ing words. . . .
GIORGIO
    Teresina, starting tomorrow you must speak like that.

The maids laugh.

TV
    . . . zeal in repeating this exercise helped your favorite actresses to achieve their success . . .
JULIET
    You know . . .
GIORGIO
    Yes?
JULIET
    This morning at the beach I was telling my doctor about what happened last night . . and . . . at one point . . . I thought . . .
GIORGIO
    What?
JULIET
    Nothing, nothing. . . .

Giorgio shrugs. Cut to the TV. A lovely girl bids her au-dience good night in a low, sexy voice.

TV
    Ladies and gentlemen, good night.

GIORGIO, appreciatively, with a slight leer, to the TV:
    Good night.

He rises.

GIORGIO

Tomorrow's going to be another busy day. Elisabetta, wake me up at seven, and have the car ready at seven-thirty.

JULIET

I'm coming up, too.

CUT

Juliet's bedroom. Giorgio lies in bed, wearing eyeshades, already asleep. Juliet hangs a thin scarf over her bedside lamp to soften the light and lies down next to Giorgio. She opens a book. Giorgio mumbles in his sleep.

GIORGIO

Gabriella . . .

JULIET

What did you say, darling?

GIORGIO

Gabriella . . .

Juliet sits up.

JULIET

Who is Gabriella? Tell me, who is Gabriella?

Giorgio sleeps quietly. Juliet bites her lip nervously.

CUT

Morning. The dining room. Giorgio, ready to leave for work, stands by the windows. He sips his coffee and sings cheerfully to himself. Juliet enters. She is still wearing her bathrobe. She sits at the table and lights a cigarette.

GIORGIO

Good morning, darling. Did you sleep well? You shouldn't start smoking so early in the morning. . . . You know, dear, I must have lunch with those people from Brazil today. I've been postponing it for two days, and it's important business. . . . What are you doing?

Juliet stubs her cigarette out in her coffee.

JULIET

You told me not to smoke, so I'm putting out my cigarette.

Giorgio walks to Juliet and kisses her on the forehead. She does not move. He begins to leave.

GIORGIO

Good-bye, my sweet. You're lovely today.

He walks to the door and stretches.

My back aches all over.

JULIET

Who is Gabriella?

GIORGIO

Who?

JULIET

Yes, Gabriella.

GIORGIO

Who? Who is Gabriella?

JULIET

Last night in your sleep you said, "Gabriella," twice.

GIORGIO

Oh, yes?

JULIET

Well?

Giorgio picks a book up from the table.

GIORGIO

Ah, here's that book I was looking for last night. Why don't you leave my things alone, where they belong?

JULIET

Last night you were dreaming. Who is she? Have I met her?

GIORGIO

Who are you talking about? I don't know. I don't know any Gabriella. You must have misunderstood. Good-bye, my little love. I'll try to get back early. In any case, I'll call. Bye-bye, Juliet. Are you going to go to the beach?

Without waiting for her to answer, he walks out. Juliet smiles at him.

JULIET

Good-bye.

Giorgio leaves, and Juliet's smile disappears. As Giorgio is seen walking briskly down the front path, we hear a voice from the TV speaking English.

TV

. . . at this point somebody knocked on the door. "Who is it?" asked the little bee. No human voice replied. Instead, a little orchestra . . .

The telephone rings.

JULIET

Elisabetta! Teresina!

Teresina comes into the room and answers the telephone.

TERESINA

Hello? . . . Hello! Go to hell!

She turns to Juliet.

I'm sorry, signora, but this happens three or four times every day. They call up, but when I answer, they hang up.

Teresina leaves. Elisabetta enters. She looks at Juliet and

smiles questioningly, as if she understood and sympathized, then raises her hands in a gesture of sad helplessness.

JULIET
    Well?
ELISABETTA
    Nothing.

She leaves. Juliet taps her fork against the table pensively, irritably.

CUT

Late morning. Juliet and her maids sit at a table set on the lawn, stringing red peppers. The maids chatter pleasantly, but Juliet does not listen.

TERESINA
    So when he comes back from Venezuela, sorry for what he's done, she says to him, "Ah, yes, you come back now, eh?"

Teresina's voice fades off. We hear Juliet's thoughts.

JULIET
    Yes, yes, I heard correctly. He said, "Gabriella." Yet he seemed so sincere when he denied . . .
TERESINA
    When someone says something, he should keep his word.
JULIET
    It is true that he likes women.
TERESINA
    Am I right, signora?
ELISABETTA
    But one should know how to be patient, too. You can't force others to do what you want.
TERESINA
    No, my dear. When someone tells me something, I believe it. When they tell me, "Yes," it should be, "Yes,"

and not, "No," and then, "Perhaps," or, "I don't know."
Isn't that so, signora?

ELISABETTA

And yet no one should be a bully . . .

JULIET

However, one time he said to me, "I'll never lie to you,
never."

The camera holds Juliet in a close-up.

CUT

Valentina walks through the gates. She wears a flamboyant
white costume and carries her tiny dog. As she enters the
yard, she stops theatrically, exaggerating an astonished delight, drops her dog, and leans dramatically against the
fence.

VALENTINA

Oh, but it's a dream! In daylight your house is a dream!

JULIET

Hello, Val. Watch the dog; there are hundreds of cats
here.

VALENTINA

What a smell! It makes you drunk! And look at the
dew! This is dew, isn't it? How pure everything is. My
heart aches, it's so beautiful. I'd love to roll naked in
the grass.

JULIET

Why don't you?

VALENTINA

Oh, no, we've become too complicated, civilized. . . .

She speaks to her dog.

VALENTINA

Hi, hi, little one! Oh, it's so wet here! Don't you mind
the dampness? Don't you get rheumatism?

Elisabetta starts to get up to give her chair to Valentina.

VALENTINA

No, dear, don't get up.

JULIET

Sit here, Valentina. Teresina, take the peppers away.

VALENTINA

Oh, you dears! What are you doing?

JULIET

We're getting the peppers ready for next winter.

VALENTINA

But you string them? Oh, a wreath of peppers! What a wonderful housewife you are! I can do absolutely nothing. What a shame. Why am I the way I am? I feel so lost, like I'm drifting. Peppers—they seem to be nothing, and yet, if I were able to prepare them, maybe I would be safe.

JULIET

Where is Teresina? Nobody has thought about lunch. Will you stay, Val? Wake up, Teresina, it's almost noon.

VALENTINA

What? Noon! I have an appointment with Raniero for eleven at the Piazza di Spagna. He thinks I'm so irresponsible, and we have such fights when I'm late. Good-bye, dear, I have to go. I'll see you at five.

JULIET

What do you mean, "I'll see you at five?"

VALENTINA

Why, didn't I tell you? I came here just to tell you. This afternoon you absolutely must come with us. Don't tell me you can't. You can't miss it.

JULIET

Where?

VALENTINA

Bhisma! Bhisma will be at the Plaza Hotel at five. He's only staying for a couple of days. Imagine, he comes to Europe only every seven years! Do you know that in America he has huge crowds of followers? Clubs, schools. . . . It's an opportunity.

JULIET

So?

VALENTINA

It's an exceptional opportunity. Don't you know his experiments?

JULIET

Never heard of them.

VALENTINA

Juliet! Where have you been? He's an extraordinary seer, an oracle, the man who holds in himself the secret of both sexes. He's unique, the only one of his kind in the world. He's an oracle who can enlighten you. He can change faces and appearances. He can tell you the real truth.

JULIET

Is he Indian?

VALENTINA

Indian, Chinese, from Tibet—it's not important. Bhisma is of the world! Good-bye, dear. . . .

JULIET

Bye-bye.

VALENTINA

Remember—these are meetings arranged by destiny. You can't miss them. Who can say that he hasn't come just for you?

JULIET

I'm sorry, but I can't come. I'd be very sorry if Giorgio called and I wasn't here.

VALENTINA

Then you'll regret it.

JULIET

Don't wait for me.

CUT

Juliet and Valentina enter the lobby of a grand hotel—large, sumptuously decorated. There are no lights on, and the lobby is dark. Faintly visible in the light of candles he holds, an old man appears at the foot of a broad stairway that climbs up into darkness.

OLD MAN
    The lights have gone out.
VALENTINA
    Where is Bhisma's apartment?
OLD MAN
    Boy! Show the ladies upstairs.

A boy comes down the stairs, lighting his way with a flash-light. Juliet, frightened, steps behind a large potted plant.

BOY
    The elevator's not working. We'll have to walk up.
JULIET
    Let's go back, Valentina.
VALENTINA
    Are there a lot of people? Has it started yet?
BOY
    I don't know.
VALENTINA
    Let's go. Have you prepared your questions?
JULIET
    What questions? I'm not going to ask anything.

Spotlighted in the beam of the flashlight, they walk upstairs ahead of the boy.

VALENTINA
    When I was a child, my father used to say that this was a hotel for kept women.

When they are almost to the top of the stairs thunder claps and lightning slashes. Valentina jumps into Juliet's arms. Spotlighted in the flashlight's beam, they hug each other.

CUT

At the top of the stairway Elena waits for them.

ELENA
    Valentina! Juliet!

JULIET

Elena!

ELENA

Thank God! I was afraid of the dark.

They hurry up the remaining steps and walk through the second floor. Juliet lags behind.

VALENTINA

Do you know that everything came true?

ELENA

Of course.

VALENTINA

During the night I dreamed about His Excellency—but he had his uniform off. What do you think that means?

Valentina and Elena walk ahead, but through the open door of a nearby room Juliet notices a wedding party in progress. She wanders off to watch.

CUT

The wedding party, seen through the open doors. A priest stands at the head of a long, festive table, around which sit a young bride and groom, relatives, guests, etc.

PRIEST

. . . Love your wife like yourself, because he who loves his wife loves himself. Love each other for better or for worse, for richer or for poorer, in health or in sickness. . . .

Juliet watches, smiling. Valentina returns and draws her away.

VALENTINA

What are you looking at?

JULIET

There's a wedding party over there.

VALENTINA

How charming.

Valentina draws Juliet toward the terrace. As they approach, we hear the first assistant's voice.

FIRST ASSISTANT
    . . . that is the second step—but it's not the illumination yet. What is this, then . . .

CUT

A broad, sunny terrace. A slightly raised platform has been set against the outside wall of the hotel. The first assistant stands at the front of the platform. His chest is covered only by an ordinary undershirt. In one hand he holds an apple out for the audience to see. Also on the platform are an Indian woman dressed in a sari and another male assistant, dressed in a suit and tie. Bhisma sits in a simple wooden chair behind a table at the rear of the platform. His hair is white, perhaps three inches long—either a man's hair grown long or a woman's cut short. He is short, plump, and old. He appears to be dozing. The first assistant holds the apple out to the audience.

FIRST ASSISTANT
    What is this, then?

The audience is composed mainly of middle-aged and old women, although several young women, a young, bearded man, and a middle-aged man are also present. They sit on chairs and stools placed irregularly in front of the platform.

YOUNG WOMAN
    It is the unique spirit, for whom everything is just appearance. But the true Buddha is beyond this distinction. Is that right?

She speaks Italian, but with a distinct foreign accent.

FIRST ASSISTANT
    That is the third step. At this point truth is at once very

near and very far away. Now, tell me: What is this?

Juliet turns to Valentina.

JULIET
Excuse me, but isn't that an apple?

VALENTINA
No, dear, you don't understand. One must see beyond the mere appearance.

The first assistant leans over to a tape recorder on the table.

FIRST ASSISTANT
Bhisma will tell us what it is.

The tape recorder begins, and we hear Bhisma's voice—old, high, quavering.

TAPE-RECORDER
It is an apple . . . only a little apple, red, and bruised on one side. At the same time it is the Buddha, the unique spirit. Things return to things. And the enlightened spirit sees the One and the Many at the same time, sees appearance and substance.

As the tape plays, the audience passes the apple from person to person, and the camera follows it. Valentina reaches for the apple and holds it against her face, caressing her cheek with it. Juliet watches her with tolerant amusement. The camera holds on Juliet together with Valentina, Elena, Dolores, and her lover as we hear:

VOICE
Do Heaven and Hell exist?

GIRL IN AUDIENCE
Who are you?

BEARDED MAN
I am an American painter.

Juliet reaches for the apple.

JULIET
Let me see. . . .

INDIAN WOMAN
Cut off my head!

CUT

The Indian woman hands a sword to the painter. The first assistant holds her by her waist, and she leans far backward, her head hanging almost to the floor, her neck stretched out, open, exposed. An old woman in the audience turns to her neighbor.

OLD WOMAN
It's a parable from the great master Lao Tse.

The painter holds the sword loosely, embarrassed, not knowing what to do. He laughs.

INDIAN WOMAN
Thus are the gates of Hell opened!

FIRST ASSISTANT
Now open the gates of Heaven!

The first assistant pulls the Indian woman erect, and they pose together, theatrically, smiling, but the second assistant interrupts them. Bhisma has slumped down into his chair. The assistants consult together for a moment speaking in German. Then, with the help of the painter, they carry Bhisma off the terrace, still in his chair. There is a whisper of puzzlement and concern in the audience, and the Indian woman comes forward, holding one hand up for silence.

INDIAN WOMAN
We won't disturb him—he is in communication with his God.

In the audience a woman turns to her neighbor.

WOMAN, speaking English:
    I was expecting this—the same thing happened to her in
Stockholm.

CUT

Bhisma's suite. In the foreground the second assistant re-
places a hypodermic needle on a bureau covered with me-
dicinal items, while in the background the first assistant and
the Indian woman help Bhisma down from a clinical table.
The suite is large and plush. Wine bottles, mostly empty,
stand on bureaus, desks, tables, and demijohns of wine, with
siphons and funnels hanging from them, are placed about
the rooms.

INDIAN WOMAN, speaking English:
    There is a lady, maestro, who needs to see you.
BHISMA
    Yes, yes. . . .

The Indian woman opens the door to the corridor.

INDIAN WOMAN
    The lady named Juliet may enter, but only she. . . .
Come in.

Hesitantly, Juliet steps into the room. She crosses the room
and sits on a sofa next to an electric fan. Its whirring can
be heard below the conversation during the rest of this
scene. Valentina, Elena, and Dolores try to follow Juliet into
the room.

VALENTINA
    Juliet, where is he? How is he?
JULIET
    He wants to see me alone. Go away.
VALENTINA
    But I brought you, you know!
JULIET
    Maybe he's in the bathroom. I don't know. He's coming

    now—wait outside.

The second assistant firmly ushers the women back into the corridor.

VALENTINA
    We have an appointment. . . .

The assistant shuts the door in her face, turns, and walks slowly across the room. He massages his temples with his fingertips. The camera follows him across the room, then swings off to Juliet. She sits nervously on the edge of the couch. She passes her hands over her forehead with weariness and worry.

CUT

Bhisma is in a bathtub. The first assistant and the Indian woman stand beside the tub, attending him.

BHISMA
    Juliet, do you know the *Kama Sutra*? Sexual relations are a conflict. To be happy one must behave like a woman. The place of conflict is the body.

CUT

JULIET
    The body?

CUT

BHISMA
    And on the body, the shoulders and the space between the breasts. Sounds to be uttered to procure pleasure are the *Hin*. . . .

CUT

The Indian woman, carrying a dish of burning incense across

the room, pauses to demonstrate the sound.

INDIAN WOMAN
    Hin!
BHISMA
    ... the great sigh ...

CUT

Elena, listening outside the door, sighs deeply.

CUT

BHISMA
    ... the sound *Put* ...
INDIAN WOMAN
    Put!
BHISMA
    ... the sound *Pat* ...

CUT

JULIET
    Pat?
BHISMA
    ... the sound Plat ...

CUT

INDIAN WOMAN
    Plat, plat, plat, plat ...

As Bhisma discourses, the camera cuts from Bhisma to the Indian woman, who demonstrates each sound; to the first assistant, who helps demonstrate bites and sounds; to Juliet's friends, listening outside the door, and to Juliet, who registers interest, puzzlement, and amusement. As the discourse ends, Bhisma is led from the bath to a large pallet laid on the floor, covered by a deep red canopy and hung with transparent mosquito netting.

BHISMA

> . . . We can add other sounds, like those of the pigeon,
> and the ducks, and the ringdove, and those of the
> flamingoes, quails, and storks. All can be used, depend-
> ing on the occasion. The different kinds of bites are the
> dark bite, the swollen bite, the point, the line of points,
> coral and jewel, the torn cloud, the wolf bite. . . .

The Indian woman and the first assistant maintain a rhythm
of echoes and demonstrative gestures. Bhisma becomes more
and more excited as he talks. Juliet becomes more nervous.

BHISMA

> Love is a religion, Juliet. Your husband is your God, and
> you are the priestess of the cult. Your spirit, like this in-
> cense, must burn and smoke on the altar of your loving
> body.

Now Bhisma is sitting cross-legged on the pallet, dressed in
white pajamas. His head hangs toward his feet, his back
bent. The first assistant and the Indian woman sit at the
end of the bed on the floor, cross-legged, like ornamental
guards.

FIRST ASSISTANT

> And now, if you have any questions, the maestro will
> be pleased to answer.

JULIET

> Well . . . nothing . . . only this—since last night I seem
> to have lost everything. I'm afraid that my husband has
> another woman.

BHISMA

> Why don't you please your husband more?

JULIET

> I do please him.

Bhisma, now transformed into a woman, throws her head
back. Her voice, high and cracked, changes, becoming a
parody of sultry seductiveness.

BHISMA

Do you remember me? I was born like this, a woman for love. Am I beautiful? Answer me frankly. Do you think I am beautiful?

Bhisma caresses her hair. She has gone into a trance.

JULIET, politely

Yes, you are beautiful.

Juliet unthinkingly caresses her hair, too.

BHISMA

I, too, think I am beautiful. Have you seen my hair? I never comb it. I caress it. I love to caress myself. I have such white skin! When I am in a bad mood, I look at my back in a mirror, and immediately I recover my good humor.

The camera moves in for a close-up of Bhisma. She rests her head sideways on her knee. Almost slyly, her large, blood-shot eyes look at Juliet.

. . . Have you bought a pair of those stockings?

JULIET

What stockings?

BHISMA

Black stockings, like net. Women want to be treated like sirens, but they don't even know their trade.

JULIET

Trade?

BHISMA

I didn't say trade. I said art.

JULIET

You said trade. I heard you. The prostitute's trade, eh? Good advice!

Juliet's bitter disagreement throws Bhisma into a wild fit. She rocks her head deep between her knees, then throws it upward, straightening her back. She moans and chokes. The camera swings to another bed, on which the second assistant lies sleeping. He rests on his back, a book open on his chest. The beautiful trapeze artist appears above him on her swing, spinning. The wind blows loudly.

BHISMA

> No! Ai! Hai! You must become beautiful like me, beautiful like me, like me, like me!

Bhisma's fit intensifies its violence. She jerks back and forth, shrieking and moaning. Close-ups catch her face in a series of horribly distorted expressions—tongue stuck far out, lips drawn back, bloodshot eyes stretched wide. She clutches at her bosom as if to exhibit it, blows a kiss that is half expectoration, and is shaken by a spasm of violent dry heaves.

CUT

A circus horse decorated with colored plumes stands on the window balcony. The wind blows, and the curtains swirl.

CUT

The sleeping assistant. The camera draws back, showing the naked legs of a woman standing astride him on the bed.

CUT

The circus horse reappears on the balcony. Now the trapeze artist sits astride it.

CUT

Close-up of Susy peeking coyly out from behind a huge hat flashes onto the screen. The wind blows violently.

CUT

BHISMA
    Is that you, Olaf? Nibur?

CUT

Juliet brushes off her clothes, as if bugs were crawling on
her. She shakes her head, "No," covers her eyes with her
hands, bites her knuckles. Beside her the fan whirrs.

CUT

Bhisma's fit climaxes in a protracted series of violent dry
heaves. Suddenly she collapses and falls halfway out of the
pallet. The wind blows and dies. The fan whirrs.

JULIET
    I want to go out! I want to go out!

The first assistant rises, utterly unperturbed.

FIRST ASSISTANT
    Be calm, signora.
JULIET
    I want to go out. I want to go out.

The first assistant leads her to the door. His posture is perfect.

FIRST ASSISTANT
    Please—it is not advisable to call up our internal forces
    without the necessary preparation. It can be very dan-
    gerous. These spirits are kind, generous, and useful—
    even though at times they give the impression that they
    are mischievous.

Bhisma picks himself up from the floor, smiling wanly. He
calls to Juliet, and she pauses before the door.

BHISMA
    Good night, signora. Did you receive a nice message?

JULIET
Yes, thank you.
BHISMA
Are you satisfied?
JULIET
Yes, thank you. Good day.
BHISMA
Good luck.

Juliet walks out into the corridor, and the door closes behind her.

CUT

Valentina and her friends surround Juliet.

VALENTINA
What did he tell you? What did he tell you? Outside here we heard . . .

The Indian woman steps out into the corridor and interrupts Valentina.

INDIAN WOMAN
Please, there is another message. He says that something new is going to happen tonight—something new and beautiful.
BHISMA, to Juliet from inside the suite:
Sangrilla quenches all thirst for anyone who drinks it . . . even that thirst which is never confessed.
ANOTHER MALE VOICE, low and smooth:
They call it the drink of oblivion.

The Indian woman returns to her suite.

CUT

VALENTINA
How strange. That wasn't his voice. It was a spirit speaking through him. Did you hear that, Juliet? He said

that you're going to have an extraordinary meeting, an extraordinary meeting tonight! Aren't you pleased, Juliet?

CUT

Inside Juliet's car. She drives; Valentina sits next to her in the front seat; Dolores and Elena sit in back. They drive along a lonely road through a thunder storm. Lightning occasionally flashes behind a range of hills at the horizon, where the road disappears.

VALENTINA
    Did you really see her?
JULIET
    Yes, I think so.
VALENTINA
    Did she say, "I am Iris"?
JULIET
    No, but I felt it was her. I felt exactly as I felt that night we were around my table.
VALENTINA
    How strange. Who can she be?
JULIET
    Who knows? Maybe she is the ballerina who ran away with my grandfather.
ELENA
    Your grandfather's dancer?
JULIET
    Yes. My grandfather was a high school teacher. He fell in love with a beautiful ballerina. . . .

CUT

The beautiful trapeze artist, Fanny, dressed exactly as at the beach and in Bhisma's suite, swings gracefully between two rows of costumed male circus attendants. The camera moves backward to reveal the circus. Elegantly dressed spectators sit in boxes surrounding the ring, protected only by long, vertical bars. Plumed horses prance gracefully around the ring. The camera moves in for a close-up of the box where Juliet's family sits: her mother, unchanged in appearance from her visit to the pine woods; her sisters, perhaps ten and twelve years old; Juliet, only six; and her grandfather, a short, robust man with a full white beard.

The plumed horses trot offstage in formation. Fanny backs out of the ring, throwing kisses, and the male attendants turn and run after her in two regular rows. Grandfather and the three children go backstage. They pass elephants, performers, other exhibits.

CUT

Backstage Fanny comes down a narrow metal staircase.

FANNY
    Oh, what a beautiful girl. What's your name?
GRANDFATHER
    Come on, Juliet, tell her your name. Do you know how daring this beautiful young lady was on stage? Yours was an extraordinary number. Accept my compliments.

Fanny smiles broadly. Her large eyes ogle him joyfully.

GRANDFATHER
    A beautiful woman always makes me feel more religious.

CUT

Little Juliet leans against the bars of a huge cage. Black Africans, clad only in breechcloths, bones, and feathers, run and leap toward her in a frenzied circus dance. She backs away.

CUT

A circus aviator climbs into an ancient biplane placed in the circus ring. The camera holds on the aviator as we hear Juliet's voice.

JULIET

. . . and, God knows why, I always thought that Grandfather and the dancer ran off in that circus plane.

CUT

Motionless, outlined against the sky on the brink of a hill, Grandfather, Fanny, the headmaster, Juliet's mother and sisters freeze in midstep, strung out single file. The line holds its frozen pose for a brief moment; then they all begin to run.

CUT

Grandfather pulls Fanny onto the aviator's outmoded plane, waiting in the middle of a beautiful green field, and they fly away.

CUT

The camera, as if aboard the airplane, shoots downward. On the field below, the headmaster, shaking his finger above his head, jumps up and down with rage.

HEADMASTER

Professor De Filippi, in the name of God, stop! I command you to come down! I am your headmaster, and you will have to give me an explanation of your abominable conduct. Professor De Filipp . . .

CUT

Juliet's car.

JULIET

He was expelled from all public schools as a result. He disappeared for a couple of years, and then he came back, as cheerful as ever. But my mother didn't want him at home any longer. I used to visit him at Christmas, but always secretly. He'd always tell funny stories. I was a little afraid of him—the bishop had told me that he was in league with the Devil. I was still a child when they took me to his funeral. Mother did not cry. I remember she wore a very beautiful black dress.

VALENTINA

What a beautiful woman your mother is.

JULIET

Oh, yes, she is very beautiful. One night I got up and met her in the corridor. She looked like a queen. Perhaps she was going to a dance with Father. . . .

CUT

Juliet's mother turns to face the camera. She is amazingly lovely, wonderfully elegant, and distinctly frightening. Makeup exaggerates her eyebrows, darkens her eyes with blue, makes her lips brilliantly red against her pale white cheeks. She looks like the evil queen from *Snow White and the Seven Dwarfs.* Unsmiling, she stares coldly ahead.

CUT

Thunder and lightning.

CUT

Grandfather's face, cheerful, winking, as if joking with a child.

CUT

Juliet's car. Her friends are all asleep.

CUT

Juliet enters the gate to her yard. It is no longer raining. She closes the gate, turns toward the house, and sees José. Tall and thin, dressed in a simple dark suit, he stands quietly,

like an apparition. Mist, as thick as dry-ice fumes, curls at
his feet. He is examining a tall rose bush. He notices Juliet,
and, as if he expects her, he walks over to her.

JOSÉ

> *Rosa aurata*, a name which is almost a good verse. I
> used to grow them once. My garden in Cordoba was
> famous. You are lucky: Flowers are grateful to those
> who care for them. It is obvious that these plants
> have received much love. If you can give so much love
> every day, your heart must be filled with love.

CUT

Close-up of Juliet, puzzled, apprehensive. He is a stranger.
Is he real? José turns and walks slowly, elegantly, back
toward the house. Near the front door a table has been set
on the lawn. On it are pitchers, glasses, dishes of fruit, and
other delicacies. Elisabetta carries a tray out of the house.

ELISABETTA

> Is that right, sir? Did you want this?

JOSÉ

> Yes, thank you.

He mixes a drink in a large pitcher.

JOSÉ

> Three slices of lemon, three of orange, mineral water.
> A glass, please.

ELISABETTA

> Here it is, sir.

JOSÉ

> No, not a champagne glass. Give me a regular glass.

JULIET

> Elisabetta, take a big glass.

JOSÉ

> Three teaspoonsful of sugar . . .

ELISABETTA

> Should I give him this one?

JULIET

Is this all right?

JOSÉ

Thank you. In Valencia they add a little clove, but in Cordoba we prefer a more delicate flavor. Please, taste it and see if you like it.

JULIET

It's excellent. What is it called?

JOSÉ

Sangrilla. They say it quenches all the thirsts of anyone who drinks it, even the thirst which is never confessed. They call it the drink of oblivion.

CUT

Close-up of Juliet. She remembers the words and recognizes the smooth, low voice.

CUT

Giorgio steps out of the house.

GIORGIO

You must stay with us at least a week. . . .

He sees Juliet.

GIORGIO

Hello, Juliet. Have you introduced yourselves? I've told you many times about my friend José. Do you remember? I was his guest in Spain.

JULIET

When?

GIORGIO

Last year, in Castile. He has a fabulous villa. You should see his paintings! Imagine. He has two Goyas. Are they Goya or Velásquez?

JOSÉ, laughing gently:

Neither. Ribera.

GIORGIO

They are magnificent. Do you know that he wanted to go to a hotel? Where else could he find the peace which we have here?

José, Giorgio, and Juliet walk into the house.

CUT

Close-up of José at the table, after dinner. His head tilted back, he talks slowly, contemplatively. His expression is absolutely tranquil, so tranquil that it seems almost to lack vitality, to be bored.

JOSÉ

> What is important is the grace of the movements, the balance. A good bullfighter must have a pure heart and clear thoughts, like a priest, or a dancer.

GIORGIO

> José has some of the most important breeding bulls in Spain. Sometimes at night this nut lights up his garden and fights and kills a bull, alone.

JULIET

> What courage! Isn't it dangerous?

JOSÉ, as calm and unmoved as before:

> It is a matter of style and poetry. Poetry is never dangerous. My best friends are bullfighters. They compose music, they write poetry. . . .

CUT

Giorgio's face. Next to José, Giorgio looks distinctly dissipated. José continues speaking. The camera moves back for a 3-shot.

JOSÉ

> They have an abhorrence for blood. The Cordoba way of fighting, for example, has an unsurpassed harmony.

He stands up, holding his cloth napkin.

JOSÉ

> Will you allow me?

JULIET

Wait—wait a second. Perhaps I have something more suitable.

She gives him her scarf.

JULIET

Is this all right as a capa?

JOSÉ

Thank you.

He walks away from the table to a slightly raised, open platform at the foot of the stairway. Juliet walks to Giorgio's side and puts her arm around his shoulders, watching José as he demonstrates.

JOSÉ

Here, look, the bull dies in his mystery. It is not the sword which kills him—it is the magic with which he is guided. I kill him with illusory blows, and the wretched bull goes into the void.

JULIET

Bravo!

José beckons Juliet to the platform, hands her the scarf, and shows her how to make a simple pass.

JOSÉ

If you miss a step, break rhythm—like a bad rhyme in poetry—then there is mortal danger. Please, signora.

Juliet holds the scarf out to try a pass. Giorgio stands up and imitates a bull, his hands held above his head as horns.

JOSÉ

A spontaneity which springs from a pure heart, clear thought, and movement precise to the ultimate degree —thus is the monster defeated.

CUT

Giorgio pulls his face into a vicious, frightening leer and charges. Juliet makes the pass, and Giorgio rushes by, but when she swings around, she hides her face against José's chest. José holds her head lightly, tenderly. Giorgio straightens up and pauses at the bottom of the stairs.

GIORGIO

Ah, I haven't shown you the present that José brought me from Spain. I'll go get it. It's splendid.

He runs up the stairs, and Juliet turns away from José, who walks to the window and begins talking pensively.

JOSÉ

Nadie comprendia de la oscura magnolia de tu vientre. Nadie sabia que martirizabas un colibri de amor entre los dientes. . . .* Do you like the poetry of Garcia Lorca? Strange twists of destiny. Yesterday I was in Madrid, and I didn't want to leave, as if I had a troubling presentiment. Now I am here, and I am very happy. What would be left in this world if we took away the harmony of an evening like this one? I'm in debt to you for this moment of real happiness. I hope it will continue.

JULIET

But for so little?

JOSÉ

A little can be everything. Yes. A quick decision, meeting an old friend by the sea, lost calm found again—everything becomes clear and plausible.

José kisses Juliet's hand. She gazes at him with wonder and warmth, but turns her head away.

CUT

Giorgio has set up a telescope in the front yard. He calls to Juliet.

---

* "No one understands the obscure magnolia in your womb. No one knows who hides a charge of love behind the teeth."

GIORGIO

> Here, come here. Isn't this a splendid present? It's magical! At any rate, it reflects the giver's taste. Here, look.

JULIET

> I can't see anything.

GIORGIO

> You haven't got it set for your eyes.

He twists a knob. Juliet looks into the telescope.

CUT

Close-up shot through the telescope. Susy caresses her hip, turns slowly, sprays herself with perfume.

GIORGIO

> Last year something very important happened over there. They give parties that the girl organizes. Last year the police broke in; they wanted to send her back to her home town. There are some fascinating stories about her.

JULIET

> She is a beautiful woman.

José shakes his head slightly from side to side in ironic tolerance of the misuse of his gift, and at Juliet's attitude.

CUT

Juliet's bedroom. Giorgio sits on the bed in his pajamas. He puts in his ear plugs.

JULIET

> Are you going to sleep right away? I wanted to talk to you.

GIORGIO, taking out one ear plug:

> Did you say something?

JULIET

> No, it's not important.

GIORGIO

> Good night.

JULIET

    Good night, dear. I'm going to read awhile, eh?

But Giorgio can't even hear this. He slides into his side of the bed, pulls his shades over his eyes, and goes to sleep. Juliet lies down, pick up a book, then hears the sound of José's footsteps upstairs.

CUT

José, still dressed, walks slowly about his room. He pauses, leans his head back, exhales a lungful of smoke.

CUT

Juliet turns out her light, but a beam of moonlight falls across her eyes. She looks straight up at the ceiling.

CUT

The front of Juliet's house. José closes his shutters.

CUT

Juliet asleep. Giorgio is not next to her. We hear Giorgio's voice coming from another room. As he talks, the camera watches Juliet awake; she looks for Giorgio, then gets out of bed and walks silently toward the kitchen.

GIORGIO

    . . . I told them to make them tobacco-colored. I told them that the most beautiful woman in the world would use them. Are you sure I didn't wake you? . . . What were you doing? . . . About me? In what way were you thinking about me? . . . Ah, ah. Good night, my love, sleep well. Until tomorrow morning. I'll wake you up. . . . Bye-bye.

Juliet stands silently in the kitchen doorway. Giorgio puts down the phone, turns around, and sees Juliet.

GIORGIO

I forgot to ask the operator to call me tomorrow morning. Luckily, I just remembered.

JULIET

Who were you calling?

GIORGIO

I told you, the operator—to wake me up in the morning.

He goes to the refrigerator, takes a bunch of grapes, and walks nonchalantly past Juliet on his way back to bed.

GIORGIO

Do you want some grapes?

JULIET

Who were you calling?

GIORGIO

What's the matter with you?

Giorgio walks off to bed. The camera holds on Juliet as she stands alone in the quiet house.

CUT

The corridor of a modern building. Juliet and Adele walk into an elevator.

CUT

Inside the elevator.

JULIET

Adele, let's come back another day—or you go alone.

ADELE

Listen, I'm not used to making a fool of myself. Now that we have an appointment, we must go.

JULIET

But to have them follow him—as if he were a thief!

ADELE

He is a thief. He stole your youth, your peace, your confidence. He is the worst of thieves.

JULIET

But a spy between me and Giorgio, one who will see everything. It will be like living with a third person.

ADELE

Aren't there already three, you poor deluded thing? Have faith in them. Think of him like a confessor. They'll arrange everything.

CUT

The corridor of another floor in the building. The elevator opens, and Juliet and Adele get out. At a corner along the hallway half of the face and body of a man leans out, a parody of the perfect dick. Juliet and Adele see him and pause. Lynx-eyes steps around the corner. He is the same man who appeared on the beach, pulling the heavy rope out of the sea. Now he is dressed like a clergyman. His huge double chin hangs over a clerical collar, and his portly body fills out his black suit. He wears steel-rimmed glasses. He introduces himself, and the women follow him down the corridor into his office.

LYNX-EYES

Good morning. You will excuse my strange mode of dress. My work often demands such transformations. We are at the service of our neighbors who need to know.

By now they have entered his office. The women sit on a bench against a wall. Lynx-eyes frees himself of the clerical collar, draws another chair close to them, sits, and leans toward Juliet with exaggerated sympathy and concern.

LYNX-EYES

Are you sure you won't be sorry later? There is still time to change your mind. You'd better stop and reflect. In similar cases I always advise a trip with the husband. Consider now the sweetness of a marriage maintained until old age, consider the tenderness of resting two white heads on the same pillow. As time passes, most problems solve themselves. Tomorrow you may be laughing at what troubles you today.

ADELE

I don't think one can laugh about one's troubles. In any case, my sister must know the truth.

Lynx-eyes is instantly ready to accommodate.

LYNX-EYES

Fair enough! I am at your complete disposal. What is this gentleman's work?

ADELE

He meets people, organizes parties . . . I don't know. . . .

She turns to Juliet.

ADELE

What *does* your husband do? I never understood it.

LYNX-EYES

Is he a public relations man, by any chance?

JULIET

Yes, yes. He organizes parties, premieres, openings of fashion shows. . . .

LYNX-EYES

Do you have some pictures of him? I must show them to our psychologist.

He turns his head and calls into another room.

LYNX-EYES

Valli!

He turns back to the women.

Now I have a very confidential question to ask you.

JULIET

Go ahead.

LYNX-EYES

You must understand that whatever is said in this office will never go beyond these walls. Now, your husband, when you look at him . . . excuse me, can you take off your glasses?

Juliet is wearing sun glasses.

JULIET

My glasses?

LYNX-EYES

Please. Thank you. When you stare at your husband, does he blush? Does he always seem to have alibis ready for any question?

JULIET

No, I don't think so.

LYNX-EYES

Have you ever surprised him on the phone while he was speaking a foreign language?

JULIET

Surprised! . . . He speaks different languages with his clients at times.

LYNX-EYES

Do you have a private language of endearments between you? What does he call you in private?

JULIET

But excuse me, I don't understand . . .

Juliet is interrupted by Valli's knock.

LYNX-EYES

Come in, Valli, I must speak to you.

Valli enters—the same thin man in the white suit who appeared in the landing barge at the beach. He wears the same suit now. He comes toward the group as Juliet continues to speak.

JULIET

I don't see what importance this can have.

LYNX-EYES

Everything is important, my dear lady, even the smallest detail. We can't neglect anything.

VALLI

Good morning.

LYNX-EYES

Mr. Valli—he is one of our most precious collaborators. Would you mind giving me the pictures of the subject?

JULIET

But is it absolutely necessary to give you his picture?

LYNX-EYES

Absolutely indispensable.

Adele hands Lynx-eyes a bundle of photographs, turning to Juliet.

ADELE

You see?

Valli takes them.

VALLI

Thank you.

He takes them to a small table, where he scrutinizes them through a jeweler's eyepiece.

LYNX-EYES

You must forgive my deplorable indiscretion, but I am not finished with my questions. Have you ever found handkerchiefs stained with lipstick? Suspicious odors of feminine perfumes?

JULIET

No.

LYNX-EYES

The smell of beauty cream? Hair which is not his on his coat? And—you'll pardon me—scratches on his body?

JULIET

No, never.

LYNX-EYES

Let's hear what our psychologist has to say.

VALLI

Judging from these pictures, I'd say he is a man from thirty-eight to forty-five years of age . . . of a nervous temperament, docile only on the surface. Successful with women. Cold angers. One must watch him because he

is capable of sudden irresponsible actions. Repressed
fears and a great need for his mother.

LYNX-EYES, jovially:

And who doesn't need his mother? . . . Now, my dear
lady, every minute of our days and nights will be de-
voted to your case. Isn't that right, Valli?

VALLI

Absolutely.

LYNX-EYES

In a week you will know everything your husband does
with his days. We have telephoto lenses which make
intimacy and secrecy outdated concepts. Neither doors
nor walls exist for us. We'll present you with an image
of your husband that you have never known about.
You'll participate in his most secret hours; you'll penetrate those shadowy portions of his life which otherwise
you could never enter.

As Lynx-eyes speaks, he rises and walks behind his desk,
where he is joined by Valli and another assistant. Lynx-eyes,
absorbed in his description of his agency's capabilities, becomes expansive, bragging. But suddenly he pauses, and his
demeanor and voice become unusually serious. He leans
forward and gazes intently at Juliet.

LYNX-EYES

. . . Are you *sure* you want to know?

It is clear that Lynx-eyes means this seriously. As he stares
hypnotically at Juliet, his face, half in shadow and half in
light, accentuates the frightfulness of the consequences.

CUT

Juliet is shaken and indecisive. Even Adele says nothing.

CUT

The headmaster appears in a corner of the office, his finger
raised admonishingly. He stands frozen, black-robed, severe.

We hear his words, but his lips never move.

HEADMASTER
> Woe to those who tolerate sin, because thus they become accomplices of the sinner, and therefore must burn with him in the eternal fires. Claim your vengeance before the Lord!

CUT

Juliet is shaken.

CUT

The headmaster stands outside the door of the office. The oval window of the door frames his stern face and gesture as if he were the picture in a cameo.

HEADMASTER
> I am the Lord of Justice.

Juliet rises and walks toward the door.

JULIET
> Yes, I want to know. It's my right, because I don't know who he is any longer, what still belongs to me, what I mean to him. I must know what he is thinking, what he is doing. I want to know everything, everything, everything!

CUT

Daytime. Juliet begins to enter her garden gate, but she sees José walking pensively about the lawn. As she watches, he stops by a garden chair, picks up a guitar, and begins to play. Juliet turns and leaves quietly. She walks into the woods.

CUT

Close-up of a heavy, big-hipped woman, almost nude, climbing onto a scaffolding which allows her to seem to be held up by the man of Charles Atlas proportions who stands beneath it.

MODEL
  I have *not* gained weight!

The camera moves back to show Dolores's studio. Huge statues, for the most part representing healthy, naked bodies, clutter the room.

DOLORES
  Oh, no? If you gain any more you'll break the platform. Juliet, do you like Nadir? How I searched to find him—and he was just downstairs. He's the doorman's son! In the refrigerator there's some chocolate. Have some. You haven't seen my new works, have you? It is not enough to look at my statues; you have to touch them. Try it. When I touch them, I feel something like a shock. I feel alive. Michelangelo shouted to his Muses, "Why don't you speak?" I would shout at these powerful statues, "Why don't you make love to me?" That's true.

Juliet sits down on a sofa, dwarfed by Dolores's statues.

DOLORES
  My art is profoundly spiritual. Shall we ever give God back his physical dimensions? Once I was afraid of God. He bothered me. He scared me. Why? Because I imagined Him theoretically, abstractly. Really, God has the most beautiful body there is. In my work I represent Him that way—physically, corporeally, a hero of the perfect form who I can desire and even take as a lover.

Juliet laughs.

JULIET

When I was a child I imagined that God was hidden in the nuns' theater, above the stage behind a large door that was always closed and was covered with dust.

CUT

The screen is almost completely blacked out by the robes of a nun. The robes hang over her loosely, so that the shape of her body is hidden. Even her face is concealed. She moves away from the camera, bends, and takes the hand of a young Juliet, a pretty girl about seven years old. They walk away from the camera down a long gray corridor, past a row of nuns lined up against the wall to their left. These nuns, too—like all the nuns who appear in this movie— are completely draped, utterly hidden by the dark robes. Each holds a pair of white, make-believe angel's wings. Young girls of about Juliet's age, all dressed in white angel's costumes, run up to the nuns. Each girl pauses while a pair of wings is attached to her back, and then trots off down the corridor, past Juliet and the other nun. The wings are attached and the girls run by with an unbroken rhythmic regularity, as if this were a ritual, or a machine.

JULIET'S ADULT VOICE

The play that year was about the life of a martyred saint. I was chosen to play her part. . . .

Camera pans along the line of nuns, now finished dispensing wings, rests momentarily on two little angels dancing gaily at the end of the corridor, then focuses on Juliet and the first nun. The nun kneels next to Juliet and peers out from behind her robes through a magnifying glass. She examines a small painting. Camera moves in for a close-up of the painting as seen through the magnifying glass. It depicts the saint being burned. Her face is that of Juliet's maid Elisabetta.

NUN

Juliet, what innocent eyes you have. You look like the saint herself.

YOUNG JULIET
> But did the saint see God?

NUN
> Yes, when she fled to Heaven among the flames of martyrdom.

CUT

Laura, in a costume of white robes, runs up to Juliet and kneels beside her.

LAURA
> Will you promise to tell me everything, Juliet, tomorrow?

YOUNG JULIET
> Yes, yes, Laura. I promise.

CUT

The adult Juliet stands in the corridor watching Laura and Juliet.

CUT

The stage. A nun in the prompter's box beckons to young Juliet.

NUN
> Come on, Juliet, it's your cue . . . .

Young Juliet is escorted to the stage by nuns. As she steps on stage, where the play is already in progress, the Emperor speaks.

EMPEROR
> Arrest her! Bring her before me. Your religion is against the laws of the Empire, but we are merciful and willing to forgive.

As the Emperor speaks the camera pans to the make-believe instrument of execution—a grillwork with spikes at both ends and short metal legs. Red streamers, tied to the edges of the grill and blown upward by hidden fans, simulate flames. Camera holds on the flaming bed until the Emperor finishes his speech.

EMPEROR

. . . Will you deny your faith? Will you sacrifice before your Emperor?

CUT

The adult Juliet stands behind the stage in the corridor. Perfectly in rhythm with the play, she answers for young Juliet.

JULIET

No, never.

CUT

The play.

EMPEROR

You prefer to die, then. You are willing to accept martyrdom?

The camera holds on the play, but it is Juliet's adult voice that answers.

JULIET

Yes, I accept it.

EMPEROR

There is still time to save your life.

CUT

The adult Juliet stands in the corridor. She answers the Emperor.

JULIET

I don't care about the salvation which you intend—I wish only to save my soul.

CUT

Young Juliet has been tied to the burning grill. She lies on her back looking upward, praying. The red streamers flap around her.

SOLDIER

Execute the Emperor's order. Burn the Christian girl!

CUT

The audience. The first row is occupied completely by nuns —a row of black, faceless robes. Behind them sit the parents, including Juliet's mother and grandfather.

CUT

Nuns off stage begin to lift Juliet into the air by turning a large winch connected to the grill by ropes that run through pulleys to the ceiling.

CUT

In the wings. Laura watches anxiously.

CUT

The grill rises toward the ceiling.

CUT

Close-up of the grill. The adult Juliet lies on it, praying.

CUT

The camera rises as if it were on the bed, focusing on a large door above the stage. The door draws closer.

CUT

The play as seen from the rear of the auditorium. While the camera holds this shot, Juliet's grandfather jumps up—between camera and stage—and strides down the aisle.

GRANDFATHER

Enough, enough! It's disgusting! Give me back my granddaughter. Juliet, get down immediately!

Juliet's grandfather climbs onto the stage. Behind him the headmaster rises from the audience and comes down to the footlights.

HEADMASTER

Professor De Filippi, enough! Come to your senses! Stop this abominable behavior!

GRANDFATHER

It's you who must stop this absurdity—I'm perfectly sane. Putting a six-year-old girl on a grill! Where are we—among cannibals?

Grandfather stomps over to the nuns controlling the winch, gesturing wildly, grandiosely.

GRANDFATHER

Let that thing down! Let it down, I said! You wretches!

He turns to the young actresses.

GRANDFATHER

Go home girls. Away with you, away, away!

He turns to the row of nuns in the audience They are filing somberly, noiselessly, facelessly out of the auditorium.

GRANDFATHER

You go up on that grill—or are you afraid to show your legs? What are you teaching these poor little girls? What are you trying to do to them, you crazy women! Go and roast yourselves on that grill!

The headmaster stands in front of the slowly passing nuns, his finger raised above his head, the very figure of fire and brimstone judgment.

HEADMASTER

    Professor De Filippi, I demand that you stop immediately! That is an order! I remind you that I'm your headmaster, that you owe me your obedience. Your behavior is abominable!

GRANDFATHER

    Oh, shut up! Abominable! . . .

Grandfather has lowered Juliet's grill back to the stage. He turns to her, still excited, but talking gently.

    And you, don't you rebel? You let them do anything they want with you? You like being burned alive, eh? Aren't you the stupid one!

Juliet reaches up to the old man's face and plays with his beard.

CUT

Laura runs out to Juliet from the wings.

LAURA

    Juliet, tell me: Did you see God? Tell me, did you see Him, did you see Him? Answer me. . . .

CUT

The headmaster and two nuns bend over Juliet's mother, who has fainted in her seat.

HEADMASTER

    I beg you, signora, forgive this embarrassing incident, which dishonors our school. . .

CUT

Grandfather leads the young Juliet away from the camera, back down the long corridor, holding her by the hand and talking to her. We don't hear his words, only the sound of a child crying. As they walk, nuns file down the sides of the corridor, forming two rows of blackness through which Juliet and her grandfather walk. The camera rolls backward between the rows of nuns so that they frame the sides of the shot.

CUT

The lawn of Juliet's home. Teresina and Elisabetta wash laundry in a large tub. Juliet is putting a permanent on a wig, set on a wooden head. She whistles happily. The gardener works on an outdoor fireplace. A cat wanders across the lawn.

JULIET
Teresina, where did that cat come from?

TERESINA
I don't know, signora, but did you see what terrible yellow eyes it has?

GARDENER
It comes from the old villa next door.

JULIET
Wait, I'll get him.

The cat jumps into a large garden pot.

TERESINA
Oh, he's gone inside.

JULIET
Gasperino, come and help us get it out.

GARDENER
I hate cats, signora.

TERESINA
Be careful, signora, he'll scratch you. Should we keep him?

GARDENER
Cats are terrible—they scratch and bite.

JULIET
Come on, they're not dangerous.

The gardener reluctantly reaches into the pot and lifts out the cat.

GARDENER
Here he is.

Juliet holds the cat against her chest.

JULIET
Oh, you're a pretty one!

She notices a name tag.

Susy, your name is Susy. . . .

CUT

Head and neck of a white peacock, close up. Camera pans to Juliet carrying the cat, seen through the iron bars of a high gate. Juliet pauses, then pulls the bell cord. A voice answers, laughing.

VOICE
The gates are open.

Juliet pushes the gates open and walks into a large, uncared-for yard. White blossoms at the ends of tall, leafless stems grow everywhere, so that it seems as if a filmy cloud of whiteness covered the ground. An expensive car, covered with leaves and dust, sits amidst the flowers. Juliet pauses, then speaks to the cat.

JULIET
What a lovely house you have!

CUT

The entrance to a large villa. The walls are in disrepair. Egyptian half-woman half-animal statues flank a short series of broad steps that lead to tall columns supporting a large portico.

CUT

Inside. Juliet enters slowly, looking curiously around her. An old woman sits on a balcony high above her, but as soon as Juliet begins to speak, she hides behind a wall. Juliet walks a few steps farther and enters an immense, high room. Its decorations, still unfinished, are wildly imaginative. The floor is partly covered with glass tiles of various colors. The walls are made of several different materials— glass, concrete, metal—and have different designs, but all nevertheless suggest a basic Arabic or Moorish design. A huge stained-glass panel representing a gigantic, brightly colored peacock dominates one wall. The colors of curtains, cushions, bottles, vases, flowers, and live parrots intensify the colorful atmosphere. Workmen's buckets and tools are lying about, and in one corner there is a pile of sand for mortar.

In the center of the room Susy lies amidst a profusion of cushions on a large bed. At its corners columns support a tent of thin, parti-colored transparent curtains that hang over the bed. Susy talks on an old-fashioned telephone as Senya, the Eurasian girl who accompanied Susy at the beach, massages her. As Juliet watches, Lola, and another woman walk toward Susy. With them is an old, stooped friar, his face wizened but cheerful.

FRIAR

    May your prosperity and health be constantly renewed. May God make you even more beautiful for His glory.

LOLA

    Tell us stories about the Barletta convent.

SUSY

    Come here for a minute. Am I good?

FRIAR

    Good? You're an angel. Until tomorrow. . . .

The friar backs out, bowing his farewells. Susy turns to an older woman who sits near her bed.

SUSY

> Will you take Alyosha away, Mother? I must finish this conversation. Hello?

Susy's mother approaches a tall, thin man who wears a white costume reminiscent of Nehru's, and begins to lead him away from Susy's bed. He resists, weeping and protesting weakly.

ALYOSHA

> Don't take me away! I don't want to go! I'm fainting!

Susy's mother leads Alyosha past Juliet. Without waiting for an introduction, she explains the situation to Juliet.

MOTHER

> He does this four or five times a day. He's foolish enough to love my daughter—come on, Alyosha! His beauty and seductiveness are all on the inside, but they don't show up on the outside. Alyosha, don't behave like this. Go on, go. . . .

Juliet walks a few steps closer to Susy, and Susy, noticing her for the first time, puts down the receiver and pulls back the curtains to greet Juliet.

JULIET

> Good morning.

Susy sees the cat.

SUSY

> What a dear you are! Where did you find that scoundrel?

JULIET

> He was in my front yard. I thought I'd bring him back.

SUSY

> How kind of you.

JULIET

> If you're not careful, he'll be stolen from you.

Susy takes the cat.

SUSY

Did you hear that? They'll steal you!

A dog lounging on her bed interferes.

You shut up. Hildegarde, take her away.

She speaks to the cat:

Where were you? Did you thank the signora? Mrs. . . ?

JULIET

Juliet.

SUSY

Oh, what a lovely name. My name is Susy. Did he behave badly?

JULIET

Oh, no, he was very good.

SUSY

Very good? Do you know he's a drunkard? He gets drunk on champagne!

She hears a faint squawking from the telephone, which lies disconnected on her bed.

SUSY

Oh, someone's waiting on the phone!

She picks up the phone and sits on the bed talking, smiling.

SUSY

It's the lady from next door. She returned the cat. . . . Of course, all my friends are pretty. . . . She might. . . . 'Bye. Excuse me, signora.

JULIET

Not at all.

SUSY

Come here. It was high time for us to meet. Stay awhile.

JULIET

Thank you, but I don't want to bother you.

SUSY

Oh, no. How would you like something to drink? Champagne? Why don't you stay for lunch?

JULIET

Oh, no, thank you, I can't.

SUSY

We'll send everybody away. I'll cook for you myself. What do you like?

She takes a bottle of champagne from a cabinet.

I can't open it. Alberto!

She tosses the bottle across the room to a beautifully built, darkly tanned young man wearing a workman's cap and a breechcloth. He catches the bottle, opens it, and brings it over to Juliet, Susy, and Senya.

SUSY

How handsome you are all covered with sweat. Don't worry—I don't want anything from you. Senya, tomorrow you must give Alberto a massage, too.

SENYA, aside, to Alberto:

I'm going to tell Susy what you did.

Alberto begins to pour champagne for all.

SUSY

Oh, good! Champagne for Signora Juliet. Live it up!

To Alberto:

Just a little for you—you know how crazy you get when you drink too much. Cheers!

To Juliet:

You'll excuse this disorder, but I'm planning some big changes—I want to make it more colorful. Would you like to see it?

JULIET

Thank you.

SUSY

And how lucky I am—I'm sure you can give me some

good advice. Welcome, Juliet!

Susy leads Juliet to a broad, curving staircase that winds upward from the center of the large room to the high balcony above. Its railings are graceful curves of bent wood. The camera follows them upstairs.

SUSY

Do you know, I once dreamed of you. It was some sort of a church. You were behind a teacher's desk, as if we were in school. I was in the last row. You were dressed like a nun, and you said to me, "Show me how you walk." I walked like this—

Susy demonstrates with a cheerful imitation of a tart's walk.

—and you flunked me. How I cried! I woke up in tears. . . . Next Saturday night we're having a party. Why don't you come? Bring your husband, of course. I see you often, from my window—I feel very tender toward you. . . . *I'd* like to love only one man—but how is it possible?

They walk along the balcony at the top of the stairs. Half-hidden behind a wall, watching the scene in the room below, sits the old woman who refused to respond to Juliet's greeting.

SUSY

Oh, here's my darling grandmother. She hasn't slept for five years. She always sits right here—and thus she sees, hears, and knows everything. Grandma Olga, this is my friend Juliet. Do you like her?

GRANDMOTHER, to Juliet:

What is the matter with you, my child?

Susy begins to walk away from the grandmother.

SUSY

I'm scared when she talks like that. She's something of

a witch, too. All she has to do is see a person and she
knows all her secrets.

GRANDMOTHER

Everything passes. . . .

JULIET

Good-bye, signora.

CUT

Outside the villa. Susy leads Juliet toward the base of a
stairway, covered with vines and leaves, all as brightly colored as if it were autumn, that climb up one wall of the villa.
A handsome, liveried chauffeur sits on the steps. He speaks
Spanish.

CHAUFFEUR

Good morning, sweet lady.

SUSY

How is she?

CHAUFFEUR

A little better, I think. But she cried all night.

Susy enters a door at the bottom of the stairs.

SUSY

It's me, Arlette. . . .

CHAUFFEUR, to Juliet:

Welcome, signora.

SUSY

Juliet, come in. . . .

Juliet enters a small room. Besides one simple bed, it has no
furnishings. Brightly colored vines grow on the walls, from
which the plaster is falling. Piles of leaves and dirt have
been left in the corners. Arlette lies on the bed, her hair cut
very short, her face turned away from the camera. Her hands
grip the headboard and the side of the bed as if she were
afraid of being torn forcibly out of it.

SUSY

> Oh, you left everything on your plate. You know what I'll do? I'll phone Signora Artemia. You don't try to resist her. Come on, get up. Get up, or I'll tell Roby to leave immediately.

Arlette sits up and faces the camera. Her expression is that of a madwoman—a combination of terror, sullenness, and utter alienation. Her short-cut hair is totally unkempt. Although she sits up, she makes no response to what happens around her. Her eyes stare wildly—but they do not see what is in front of her.

SUSY

> Be calm, Arlette. This is a friend of mine. She likes you. You like her, Juliet, don't you?

JULIET

> Yes, of course.

Susy mixes some medicine into a glass of water.

SUSY

> Here, drink this. Why won't you believe that all of us love you? I'll come back soon. Good-bye.

Susy leads Juliet out of the room and up the outside stairs.

JULIET

> What is the matter with her? What did she do?

SUSY

> She tried to kill herself three times. The last time I was just in time to save her. I telephoned her, but no one answered. We had to break down her door. You should have seen the mess she was in. She is very unlucky in love.

JULIET

> That's like Laura, a school friend of mine. She drowned in a canal. She was fifteen. They said it was an accident, but she killed herself. She committed suicide for love.

As Juliet finishes her reminiscence, Susy stops and listens outside a door at the top of the staircase.

LOLA'S VOICE
Here, take this one—it even has feathers.

Susy rushes angrily into the room. Lola has just given Alyosha one of Susy's shoes.

SUSY, to Alyosha:
What are *you* doing here? Now I'm really fed up with you!

She grabs the shoes back.

SUSY
Excuse me.

A MAID
I told him you'd get mad at him. I know you get mad.

SUSY
I told you that you can't come in here. Do you understand? I don't want you taking my things.

Lola comes toward Susy. She carries a vase of purple flowers.

LOLA
It was only a slipper.

At Lola's remark Susy breaks into a sudden, violent rage.

SUSY
I don't want him to! I'm the boss of this house, and if you don't like it, you can go back onto the street!

Juliet stands bewildered in the doorway. Susy turns to her and gestures toward Lola.

SUSY
She was in a whorehouse, this one was.

LOLA
You'd love to be in a whorehouse, too.

Susy turns around to face Lola.

SUSY

What?

She begins to laugh, suddenly cheerful and friendly.

SUSY

Absolutely! Why not?
To Juliet:

If you could only hear what stories she tells, this bitch.
They're all made up, of course. We're only joking. What
else could it be besides joking?

Lola leaves her flowers on a small table. Camera moves in
for a close-up of the flowers, and we hear the voice of Iris.

IRIS

Juliet, how are you? I've kept my promise. Susy will be
your teacher. Listen to her.

CUT

Juliet, listening. Her thoughts are interrupted by Susy, who
stands talking, more quietly, to Alyosha.

SUSY

I can't encourage your fetishism, Alyosha. Yours is
nothing but fetishism. Momy explained it to me. But
now I'm going to give it to you, anyway.

She gives the shoe back to Alyosha, who backs out of the
room gushing grateful Russian. Susy turns her back to
Alyosha, generously twitches her behind for his pleasure,
then walks toward Juliet.

SUSY

I don't think that it's good to be a fetishist, and it must
be terrible for a Russian. Oh, come look here!

Juliet walks to the window at which Susy stands. The camera

looks out the window at Juliet's house—quiet, simple, neatly kept. The maids and the gardener work happily in the yard.

SUSY

... How many times I've watched you in your yard. ...

Juliet lingers before the window until Susy calls her.

CUT

Susy lies on a huge, round bed, looking up into a mirror of the same shape and size attached to the ceiling directly above.

SUSY

Come here, Juliet. Do you have a mirror like this, too? Do you like it? I had it put there—Momy loved the idea. It's like having four in bed. I don't know what you must be thinking of me—but, you know, men have such strange whims.

Juliet lies on the bed next to Susy, looking up at the mirror. The mirror seems to take her fancy. She lies smiling, bemused, until her thoughts are interrupted by Susy's shouts.

SUSY
Juliet!

Her voice echoes, as if coming through a long tunnel. Juliet sits up, but Susy is not in the room. Juliet notices a hole that has been cut in one wall of the room, its edges decorated to look like a scallop's shell. She walks to the hole and looks in. A slide runs down from the opening to a swimming pool below. Susy swims, naked, at the end of the slide, and calls up to Juliet.

Join me, Juliet—the water's warm. This is another one of my ideas. After we make love, my boyfriend and I slide down. It's wonderful. Come on, Juliet. Take off your clothes.

JULIET

No, thank you.

SUSY

Once Momy slid down headfirst, got stuck, and almost died. Come on, Juliet, dive in.

CUT

Susy, dressed in a skimpy black bikini, visible through a thin veil that hangs down to her thighs from a huge, flamboyant hat, leads Juliet through the pine woods. Juliet wears a red sweater and white slacks. Both ride on small, two-wheeled children's bikes. They bicycle to a large tree, under which Susy stops.

SUSY

I accept everything. I deny myself nothing. . . .

Juliet points up into the tree.

JULIET

Look up there! What's up there?

SUSY

. . . I dance, eat, gamble, fight—I love to fight. Let's go sunbathe a little—up there. It's much better than the beach—a personal sun, all mine. Look on the tree trunk, Juliet; there's a switch.

JULIET

But are we going up there?

SUSY

Of course. Push down the lever.

As Susy speaks, a large basket is lowered from above, at the end of a heavy rope. She climbs in, Juliet throws the switch, and Susy slowly ascends, still chattering.

SUSY

In Greece there is a monastery on a mountain, and the monks get up just like this.

The basket stops at a wooden platform built around the trunk of the tree, high above. Susy climbs out.

SUSY

Send it down.

JULIET

What should I do? Push it up?

SUSY

Yes, good. Now it's your turn.

Juliet climbs into the basket.

Ready? Don't be afraid. Are you dizzy? Close your eyes.

Juliet reaches the platform.

SUSY

Give me your hand.

JULIET

No, thanks, I can manage by myself.

Juliet, dizzy, climbs gingerly out of the basket. Susy's tree-house is high up in a tall, straight tree—a large octagonal platform ringed by screens, windows, and sun reflectors, and equipped with a liquor cabinet.

SUSY

They can go on chasing us as long as they like. They won't find us here.

JULIET

Who?

SUSY

Those two guys following us. Didn't you notice? . . . The other day there were two lovers down there in the bushes. They kept on making love. I wanted to applaud. They were marvelous. And from up here everything seemed so delicate, so joyful. Are you still dizzy? Now let's drink something. The sun is at its zenith—it's the finest hour of the day. You don't project any shadow.

She reaches into the cabinet and takes out a glass.

SUSY

Oh, it's full of rainwater! There are two minnows inside. Sit down—let's drink. Let's sunbathe naked.

JULIET

No, thanks, I'm all right like this.

Susy takes off her hat and veil and lies on her back. Juliet sits, fully clothed, next to her.

SUSY

Grandma makes strange perfumes from herbs from the woods. I'll let you try them—they make men drunk. Once there was an engineer . . .

She sighs as she remembers.

SUSY

What were you saying about your marriage?

JULIET

Oh, nothing.

SUSY

You don't trust me.

JULIET

Yes, but . . .

SUSY

Well, tell me.

JULIET

Have you ever thought of marrying?

SUSY

No, never.

JULIET

I was saying that I always thought that marriage should be like this: I should be all for him, he all for me. I'm almost ashamed to admit it, but Giorgio was my first love. As soon as I saw him I fell in love and didn't want anything but to live with him, and when he asked me to marry him, I was so happy I couldn't believe it was true. He became my whole world—my husband, my lover, my father, my friend, my house. I didn't need anything else. I thought I was happy. . . .

Susy has been looking down through the basket hole in the

platform. Two young men in a sports car stop under the tree.

SUSY

Ahhh.

BOYS, below:

They must be at the beach. They've disappeared.

Susy, using her mirror, flashes a ray of sunlight on them, catching their attention.

BOYS

No, look, up there!

JULIET

What are you doing?

SUSY

They've found us. Those naughty boys!

BOYS, calling up from below:

We've got something very important to tell you.

JULIET

Do you know them?

Susy dangles a shoe over the hole.

SUSY

Not at all. . . . I was supposed to be married when I was thirteen. . . .

She lets go of the shoe.

SUSY

Oh! I dropped my shoe!

JULIET

I'm sorry, but I'm late. I must go back home.

SUSY

So soon?

JULIET

Will you let me down, please?

Juliet climbs into the basket and descends. Susy stays in the treehouse.

SUSY

    Good-bye, Juliet. Come back anytime you want to.

Juliet arrives at ground level. The boys help her out.

BOYS

    Good morning. How are you? Let me help you out. Are you going already?

Juliet nods that she must go and walks a short distance off, then turns to watch the two boys climb into the basket and ascend together.

BOYS

    Hoopla! I'm getting off at the first floor.

The camera shoots up past the rising basket and through the hole in the platform through which the basket passes. Susy stands, greatly foreshortened, on the edge of the hole, her legs set wide apart, one arm held over her head, one hand on her hip, smiling broadly.

Juliet watches, smiles, shakes her head, and walks away.

CUT

Juliet's yard. Her two nieces sit on the lawn, listening to Juliet, who is cutting flowers and handing them to Teresina as she tells them a story.

JULIET

    . . . and, among all these trials, there was also the one in the labyrinth—the hardest of them all. A labyrinth is a huge palace where, if someone enters, it is impossible to find the way out. The more one wanders around, the worse it gets. . . . Teresina, what's wrong with you today?

TERESINA

    I'm a little depressed, signora.

NIECE

    Aunt, then what happened?

TERESINA

 May I leave a little early today, signora?

JULIET

 Well, Seven-in-One-Blow, who was not even afraid of
 the Devil, said, "I'm going to enter the labyrinth." . . .
 All right, you may go, Teresina . . . "But what will you
 give me if I come out of it?" . . . I don't like this business of going out every day from three to eight—I don't
 like it a bit. . . .

Juliet leads her nieces into the house, continuing the story.

JULIET

 . . . And he crossed the woods, which were full of
 golden apples. There were so many golden apples and
 they were so shiny that even at night the woods were
 lit up.

The telephone rings. Juliet steps inside and answers it.

JULIET

 Hello?

LYNX-EYES' VOICE

 Is the lady of the house in?

JULIET

 Speaking.

LYNX-EYES

 Lynx-eyes here.

JULIET

 Just a minute, please.

She turns the nieces toward the door.

JULIET

 Go and play outside. I'll come in a second. Hello?

LYNX-EYES

 Can you stop by this afternoon?

JULIET

> Today? I can't. . . . But how? . . . Have you found something already?

LYNX-EYES

> We've had seven very hard days, but I believe that you'll appreciate our work.

JULIET

> Can't you tell me over the phone?

LYNX-EYES

> Well, it is not our policy. You must understand.

JULIET

> Of course.

LYNX-EYES

> Till this afternoon, then.

JULIET

> I'll try.

LYNX-EYES

> My warmest regards. . . .

CUT

Juliet enters the office of Lynx-eyes. With methodical calmness but without a pause, Lynx-eyes greets her, seats her, reassures her as he arranges the equipment—a movie projector, a screen, etc.—and simultaneously launches into his spiel.

LYNX-EYES

> Good morning, signora. Here we are. I think I can tell you that we have gathered some great pieces of information. Valli will show you all that you wanted to know.

Valli sets up the movie screen.

LYNX-EYES

> I understand your anxiety, my dear lady, but always remember—nothing is definite, nothing is irreparable. Please sit down. If you only knew how many couples have been reconciled right here in this office!

Valli has poured an aperitif, which he now offers to Juliet.

VALLI

    Something to drink, signora?

Juliet shakes her head no, and Valli drinks it himself.

LYNX-EYES

    On the other hand, the only way for two people to love
each other truly is by knowing each other thoroughly
—Saint Augustine says this very thing. Don't consider
this an unhappy day. . . .

Valli turns off the lights and starts the film. Juliet sits stiffly
next to the projector, watching Giorgio and a lovely young
woman romp across the screen. As the film runs, the camera
cuts back and forth between the screen and Juliet. Without
moving, she begins to cry, soundlessly.

LYNX-EYES

    Perhaps the photography is not always perfectly clear
—but you can imagine the conditions under which our
collaborators worked most of the time.

VALLI

    These are the first three days of the investigation, from
the twenty-third to the twenty-fifth. . . .

LYNX-EYES

    If you will permit me, I'll read the report concerning
the film. "Day: twenty-third. The subject leaves home at
seven-thirty. He's wearing a white suit. He's followed
by a car from home to a florist. . . ." It goes without
saying, of course, that we have the name and address
of the girl who received these flowers. Right here, if you
want them.

VALLI

    Here we are filming at the restaurant. . . . Her big hat
didn't allow us to show the girl's face. . . .

LYNX-EYES

    Please understand, signora. I always ask clients to re-
gard everything we show them with a certain detachment. Ours is an objective point of view, and therefore

limited. Reality at times may be quite different, more innocent. . . . Is this Lake Bracciano, Valli?

VALLI

No, it's a field below the Castelli. This was taken on the twenty-fourth. An afternoon ride, twenty-seven kilometers out on the Appian Way. They stopped in the country from 4:20 to about 6:00 P.M. The girl is Gabriella Olsen—twenty-four years old, profession: model. . . . While we change reels, let's look at some slides. Grillo?

Another assistant comes in and begins running the slide projector.

LYNX-EYES

I took these myself. . . . Please turn on the tape recorder. We've recorded the conversation of the two subjects while they were in the car near the park.

The slides flash rapidly on the screen, showing Giorgio and his girlfriend talking gaily, embracing, kissing, smiling.

CUT

Juliet cries silently. Camera continues to cut between Juliet and the screen as we hear the taped voices of Giorgio and Gabriella.

GABRIELLA

God, God. . . . You're confusing me with someone else. When you met me, you had . . .

GIORGIO, interrupts her, singing:

When I met you, when I met you, when I met you, the moon was shining. . . . You should be flattered by what I'm telling you. Like an idiot I'm letting you know how jealous I am. I can't stand him! . . . You're perfect! . . .

LYNX-EYES

The interpretation of this, signora, is up to you. We're just showing it to you. The material belongs to us, as stated in the contract. It can be shown and used in the case of a legal separation and under the request of a judge. As you must know, signora, we have had expenses—materials, per diem, overtime—everything is here. The bill is at your disposal. We'd like you to know that we've given your case special consideration.

Valli has begun to run the movie projector again, but Juliet is no longer watching. She stands up between the projector and the screen, her shadow blocking out an image of Giorgio and Gabriella embracing in a country meadow, and begins to leave.

JULIET
Thank you. Good night.

She walks out as Lynx-eyes speaks.

LYNX-EYES
Good-bye. Allow my collaborators and myself to wish you our best. We hope that everything will turn out according to your wishes. . . .

CUT

The entrance to Susy's villa. The chauffeur sits on the steps. He rises and speaks in Spanish.

CHAUFFEUR
Good evening, signora. May I wish you a pleasant evening?

CUT

Inside. More women than men lie or sit about the large room on cushions and sofas. The women's dresses are wild, extravagant, colorful. The camera pans over the guests, then swings back to show Juliet entering. She wears a red dress and top piece which is somewhat livelier than anything she has worn so far, but it is in no way comparable to the costumes of the other guests. Susy lies on her canopied bed, talking to a man.

MAN

Look, it's your charming neighbor.

Susy looks up, smiling happily, and walks across the room to · greet Juliet.

SUSY

Juliet! I knew you'd come. How are you?

JULIET

Fine.

SUSY

And your husband? Did you send him to bed without his supper? . . . Hello, Margy.

MARGY

Hello. Listen, Susy, when will we begin?

Susy laughs.

JULIET

He hadn't come back yet. He always comes back late. He works, he works hard. So I came by myself. He trusts me completely.

SUSY

He shouldn't do that at all.

Susy leads Juliet across the room. They pass Susy's mother, sleeping in a chair.

SUSY

. . . You know my mother. I won't wake her, or she'll · start singing. . . .

She leads Juliet through some gauze curtains into a section of the room where several men sit on cushions around a low table. They are playing a game of dice. She speaks to one of the players, a heavy, swarthy man with a bald head.

. . . Momy, this is Juliet.

MOMY

Thank you, my lady, for honoring my house.

Momy is clothed completely in white, in a costume that suggests the modern dress of India. The camera focuses on him only from behind, showing his bulk. As he greets Juliet, he turns his head and we see one side of his large face. He wears sun glasses. Susy and Juliet walk away.

SUSY

Do you know who that is? That's Momy, my fiancé. He's sixty-five. Do you know, he wants to make love every day? And he does. . . . What's the matter? You have such a sad look.

JULIET

I'm fine. In fact, I really want to enjoy myself tonight.

SUSY

Good! I want to embrace everybody! I want you to be happy.

She gives Juliet a drink.

SUSY

Here, take this.

CUT

The party. There is no dancing and little conversation, but now activity increases. A short, thin man with a goatee walks across the room reciting something in French. The camera follows him and slips off him to a young woman who begins to declaim in English.

YOUNG WOMAN

I am the East Wind, that opens the gates of the heavens, that frees the Wind of the West, that speeds the sun on its way. This is the wind of life. This is the wind of the Orient. . . .

As she recites, the camera pans across several of the guests' faces . . . an old, thin woman, her hair cut short . . . the man with the goatee walks past behind her and rubs two fingers across her scalp . . . a woman heavily rouged, lips red, shiny . . . the face of the thin man with the goatee. He commands attention.

MAN WITH GOATEE

Attention! This is the most intimate, most secret moment. . . .

He points to a man lying on his back on a table, either asleep or hypnotized. Three women lean over him.

CUT

Juliet, smiling as she watches. She takes a swallow of her drink.

MAN WITH GOATEE

. . . Here is an old Egyptian rite for the passage from life to death. . . .

CUT

Lola and two other women are slowly descending the broad staircase. One of them walks ahead of the other two. She is older, heavily made up, and luridly rouged. She wears a huge white wig and carries a fan of large, brightly colored feathers. She reaches the bottom of the stairs and walks into the party, reciting in Italian, but with a foreign accent.

WOMAN

I am the Goddess of Vice. An hour with me might kill you—but you'd see the heights and the depths. This is my hour—at eleven at night I reach the peak of my desire. . . .

CUT

Susy is with Juliet. They watch the woman recite, and laugh together.

SUSY
    It's a game we play in Lola's honor. We recreate the
    atmosphere of a house of pleasure.
JULIET
    It's interesting.

CUT

Lola has reached the bottom of the stairs. We pick up a
fragment of her conversation.

LOLA
    . . . then you look into his eyes. . . .

She walks over to a man sitting alone.

    . . . This one with the beautiful big nose. . . .

She twitches his nose, then walks over to another man.

    . . . This gentleman hasn't chosen yet?

She sits in his lap.

CUT

A beautiful young woman whose costume seems to be composed solely of long black feathers walks across the room.

WOMAN WITH FEATHERS
    Is this all right?
LOLA
    Perfect!

The young woman walks toward Juliet and Susy.

CUT

Momy, his back to the party, plays dice. The camera pans to
the thin man with a goatee. Now he performs another rite,

this time with a young woman dressed only in a white sheet. A white handkerchief is tied over her eyes.

MAN WITH GOATEE
Kneel down.

She kneels down before him.

What is your name?
YOUNG WOMAN
Hildegarde.
MAN WITH GOATEE
No, your name is Sex. What is your name?
HILDEGARDE
Sex.
MAN WITH GOATEE
No, your name is Womb. What is your name?
HILDEGARDE
Womb.
MAN WITH GOATEE
No, your name is that of the divinity. You are no longer yourself. You are the door and the earth, the corolla, the crown of the goddess.

The kneeling woman falls to the floor. As the rite ends, the camera pans around the room. Most watch the rite performed, although no one seems very deeply involved. Others seem notably disinterested. They stare away in other directions, faces blank, as if drugged or completely disoriented. One girl looks away from the rite, crying.

CUT

Juliet, Susy, and the young girl dressed in feathers.

JULIET
Are you a model?

The girl seems hypnotized. Her eyelids are almost closed;

she sways her head slowly, in an exaggerated rolling movement. She answers haltingly, as if talking were difficult or
boring.

MODEL
    Yeesss. . . .
JULIET
    Do you know someone called Gabriella?
MODEL
    Yeesss. . . .
JULIET
    Gabriella Olsen. Is she very beautiful?
MODEL
    Yeesss . . .
JULIET
    Much more beautiful than I am?
MODEL
    She's very . . . very beautiful. . . .
JULIET, tartly:
    She's also a little bit of a slut, too, isn't she?

The model, who has been swaying her head slowly from
side to side, suddenly stops and stares at Juliet, shocked, as
if to say, "What is someone like this doing here?"

JULIET
    . . . You can be frank with me—that's almost become a
    compliment for me.

Susy watches Juliet closely. She bends over Juliet and whispers in her ear.

CUT

Juliet climbs halfway up the stairs, then turns around, raises
her arm in a theatrical gesture, and calls to Susy.

JULIET
    Do I play the part well?

SUSY

Isn't she perfect!

Juliet walks down a few stairs, showing herself off, smiling. She pauses, assumes another pose, and notices Susy's grandmother, sitting in her niche in the balcony. Juliet freezes and forces a slight nod. Suddenly she is upset.

CUT

The party. The scene and the atmosphere have changed completely, as though several hours had passed. Now only a few people lounge about the large room. A tall, voluptuous Negro girl dressed in a skintight, transparent, spangled net costume sprawls lazily on the floor. She begins to sing in a strong, low voice—a muted, sexual, seductive song.

CUT

Juliet sits on the steps looking down at the party through the banister. Her face is very sad. She forces a smile.

CUT

The Negro girl, singing, runs her hands along her body.

CUT

Arlette sits alone on a sofa, staring straight before her. Her eyes and her face are immobile, insane.

CUT

The other guests. All their faces are thoughtful, moody, depressed.

CUT

A beautiful young man dressed in the same white costume Alyosha and Momy wear enters the room. He walks past several women, including Arlette. They look up at him and smile. Arlette stares fixedly at nothing. The young man goes up to Momy, bends, kisses his hand.

CUT

Juliet watching from the stairs.

CUT

SUSY, below, calls up to Juliet:
    He's my godson. Isn't he handsome?

Her godson kneels beside Susy.

CUT

Juliet nods to him, smiles, then waves to him. He nods in reply, as Susy bends over to whisper in his ear.

CUT

The large room is completely empty, except for a couple walking slowly away.

CUT

Juliet still sits on the stairs. We hear Susy's voice, whispering.

SUSY
    Juliet, come on, I'm up here. . . .

Juliet climbs the stairs. As she reaches the top, she leans against the wall, weary and somewhat drunk.

CUT

Darkness, outside. A man and a woman lean against the wall, kissing. Suddenly illuminated in the beam of a flashlight, the woman looks into the camera, lipstick smeared across her chin and cheeks, smiling wildly. She winks, then makes a sound that is half laugh and half gasp.

CUT

Susy holds a flashlight, laughing. She leads Juliet up the outside stairway. As they climb, Susy spotlights couples embracing in the foliage along the stairs and on the balcony.

Spotlighted, the model tears her lips away from her man and whispers hoarsely, "Get away!"

A large woman leans over the short thin man with the goatee, her back to the camera. He leans back against the wall, eyes closed, arms hanging limply, against his sides, as if exhausted.

Light shines through the window of Arlette's room, catching her climbing onto a bed where a man lies unmoving on his back. Her face contorted, she claws at the air, angrily gesturing at him to leave. She laughs harshly.

Susy shines the light on Juliet.

SUSY
    He's waiting. He wants you.

Juliet blinks, smiles vaguely. They climb the remaining stairs and enter Susy's bedroom. Two maids prepare Juliet for love. One holds up a mirror for her; the other sprays her with perfume. They leave the room. Susy blows a kiss to Juliet and leaves. Lola pauses at the door.

LOLA
    There's the champagne!

CUT

Juliet is alone. She walks to the huge round bed and sits on its edge, looking down the slide to Susy's pool. She sips champagne.

CUT

Susy's godson stands on the balcony. He walks slowly toward Juliet and sits beside her on the bed.

CUT

Lola, the maids, Susy, and all the women Juliet passed on the stairs listen in the darkness outside the bedroom.

CUT

The bedroom. The shell-shaped tunnel of the slide. We hear the voice of Iris.

IRIS
   Juliet! Susy is your teacher. Listen to her; learn from her.

CUT

Susy's godson, close-up. His eyes and mouth are almost sweet and gentle, but his eyebrows are demonic. He looks at Juliet.

CUT

The camera shoots through the overhead mirror down onto the couple sitting on the edge of the bed.

JULIET
   Perhaps I drank too much.

Suddenly we hear the loud whisper of a little girl.

LITTLE GIRL
   Juliet! What are you doing?

CUT

The camera shoots up from the bed. Seen in the mirror above, as if standing on a balcony, is a young girl dressed in white nightgown and nightcap surrounded by leaping flames. Behind her are the upright iron bars of the grill. The girl stands slightly in front of the bars, her hands raised slightly from her sides, palms out—it is Elisabetta. Her hair is blond, but she is in exactly the same position and has the same facial expression she assumed when earlier she tried to communicate her sympathy to Juliet. Sound of wind blowing.

CUT

Juliet, terrified, jumps from the bed and runs to the wall. Slowly she edges along the wall, whimpering.

CUT

Susy's godson sits on the bed watching Juliet, puzzled.

CUT

The martyr burns before the upright grill above the ceiling. Close-up of her face—Elisabetta's. Wind.

CUT

The faces of Lola and Susy as Juliet runs past them, down the stairs.

SUSY
    Juliet!
MAID
    Signora!

CUT

In the light of early dawn, Juliet runs through Susy's overgrown yard, past a statue with the breasts of a woman and the beak of a monstrous bird.

CUT

A bright afternoon. Juliet's nieces, blond and pretty, dressed in pure white, frug on a bright green lawn. Giorgio and Juliet are giving a lawn party. Valentina enters, dressed in a completely white outfit similar to a young girl's confirmation gown. She embraces Elena, who sits on a small settee.

VALENTINA
    I'm terribly late, aren't I?
ELENA
    How are you?
VALENTINA
    Have you seen Juliet?
ELENA
    No. I haven't seen her. Where are you going—to be confirmed?

Valentina greets Juliet's doctor, who sits cheerfully surveying the party.

VALENTINA
    What are they doing?
DOCTOR
    They're psychoanalyzing my wife.
VALENTINA
    Is it the American doctor?

Camera pans to Dr. Miller, an American woman, talking to Juliet's doctor's wife.

DR. MILLER
    Now, begin to concentrate. Try to remember what's deep within you. . . .

CUT

Giorgio, Juliet's mother, and Adele sit together at a small table. Giorgio speaks to Juliet's mother.

GIORGIO

I'm curious about what will happen when it's your turn.

MOTHER, laughing:

Oh, no—very dangerous.

GIORGIO

I know—you're scared.

MOTHER, laughing flirtatiously:

No, Giorgio, for goodness' sake!

Giorgio rises and starts to go into the house, but pauses to listen to Dr. Miller explain psychodrama.

DR. MILLER

In any psychodrama each participant must be a vehicle for truth. It is necessary to create an atmosphere of total, absolute truth.

DOCTOR'S WIFE

I don't think that I'm the right person.

DR. MILLER

Try to reconstruct in front of us here that scene when you were scolding your son-in-law.

She points to the lawyer, who sits at another table playing cards.

Ah! Would you like to play the son-in-law?

DOCTOR'S WIFE

The attorney is too old for that.

LAWYER, joking:

Thank your for the compliment, signora.

Dr. Miller walks over to a settee on which Dolores, Genius, and Dolores's lover are sitting. She draws the lover away.

DR. MILLER

All right. Let's try this handsome young man. He will certainly be better.

GENIUS

> I was just reading his hand!

Dolores walks away. She takes some grapes from a table amply covered with fruit and food.

GENIUS

> . . . Where are you going? I don't understand . . . Aren't you interested in the future? Come here!

DOLORES

> No—I'm only interested in what happens to me here, today, now.

CUT

Elisabetta stands burning before her grill, framed by two bowls of fruit on the refreshment table.

CUT

Juliet turns away from her bedroom window, whispering to herself.

JULIET

> Forgive me! I'll never do it again.

Elisabetta walks by outside the window and notices Juliet.

ELISABETTA

> Signora. They're waiting for you.

JULIET

> Yes. I'm coming.

Juliet opens a closet door. A huge bare breast confronts her. The sound of wild laughter. She slams the door, distraught.

JULIET

> Enough! Leave me in peace! Leave me in peace!

Juliet walks into her bathroom. The camera, still in the bedroom, flashes a quick shot of Elisabetta burning on the grill. The wind blows loudly.

CUT

Juliet begins her toilette in the bathroom.

CUT

A small, round window in the bathroom wall. It is covered with brightly colored foliage, as on the outside stairs leading up to Susy's bedroom. Susy's face peeks through the foliage. Juliet stares at the window, backing slowly away. Stealthily, she reaches for a glass and suddenly throws it at Susy's face. The foliage fades, leaving Susy's face which remains for a brief moment, smiling, and then also fades, leaving only a broken window. Juliet tries to continue dressing. We hear a voice moaning Juliet's name, and the camera pans to the wall next to the round window. Slumped against the tile wall amidst the broken glass sits a young girl in a white nightgown and cap—apparently the girl who burned on the grill a few moments ago. Her face is invisible because her head hangs forward. Slumped like a broken doll, her chin is propped against her chest. Her hands lie, palms upward, beside her, unmoving. Juliet steps toward her as if to help, but as she draws near, the girl throws her head up, baring Susy's breasts and Susy's face, laughing madly. Juliet backs away.

JULIET

You shameless liar! I won't believe a word you ever say to me—never! Go away! Go away!

CUT

Teresina is alone on the lawn. She waves to a man disappearing through the trees.

TERESINA

Go away!

Juliet runs to the window.

JULIET

Teresina, who are you talking to?

TERESINA

Nobody, signora.

JULIET

Who were you talking to?

TERESINA

Nobody.

The camera focuses on the foliage outside the fence at the edge of Juliet's lawn. A nearly naked woman smiles, partly hidden behind a tree. One of the ferocious Africans who danced at the circus peeks out from behind another.

CUT

The plump rump of the nearly naked woman, close-up. Her body is covered only by flowered net tights that conceal nothing. She is one of the women who appeared in the landing barge. Swinging her purse, she walks away from the camera, through the trees.

CUT

Juliet's face.

Giorgio calls to Juliet from outside the bathroom door.

GIORGIO

Juliet! Come on, everybody's waiting for you.

CUT

The party. Sylva talks to Dr. Miller.

SYLVA

Let me do a psychodrama. I have a shadowy episode in my life that . . .

Juliet comes out of the house.

ELENA
>Good afternoon, Juliet.

JULIET
>Hello, hello! Hello, everybody.

SYLVA
>Hi!

JULIET
>Hello, Mother.

Giorgio, Adele, and Juliet's mother sit together at their table. Giorgio pulls a settee next to his chair.

GIORGIO
>Sit down. Do you want something to drink?

JULIET
>No.

But she takes the drink that Giorgio offers her. Giorgio seems remarkably attentive to Juliet.

GIORGIO
>Dr. Miller has proposed a new game. You have to re-live difficult episodes of your life by projecting them onto someone else. Interesting, eh?

JULIET
>Yes.

ADELE
>Really, Juliet! Some of your guests!

JULIET
>Hello, Adele. . . . Cheers, Mother.

MOTHER, coolly:
>Your kimono is very nice, but your eyes are red. You've been crying. . . . I find these games *so* boring.

Genius walks over to Juliet's group.

GENIUS
>Don't fly on the twenty-seventh. . . . May I say hello to the hostess? And how pretty you are—but, of course, with a mother like this!

To Adele:

>Ah, you are going to have a boy—yes, a boy. Remember, dear lady, that I predicted it.

Valentina comes up to Juliet.

VALENTINA

>Look, Juliet, why don't you play the game? You, with such a sad face. . . .

She draws Juliet away from the table.

>Quiet, everybody! The next turn will be Juliet's.

GIORGIO

>Maybe Juliet doesn't feel like playing.

JULIET

>Yes, yes, I feel all right. I want to try.

VALENTINA

>She wants to! She wants to! It's a fantastic experience. You'll feel liberated.

She leads Juliet over to Sylva and Dr. Miller.

SYLVA

>It's like seeing yourself in a mirror. With Dr. Miller, you begin to understand your neuroses.

DR. MILLER

>Tell us about an episode in your life that was painful for you. Try to recall for us the place of this story, the circumstances. We want to . . .

JULIET

>Is it true? Can you really help me?

The sound of wind. Val and Sylva run to a nearby bench, sit next to each other, whisper a moment, and settle back to watch. The camera pans to follow them. Behind them Elisabetta burns before the upright grill.

JULIET

>They've started again!

The camera swings to a nearly naked man with a long red

beard. He stands motionless, half-hidden behind a bush.

CUT

Behind Giorgio, Adele, and Juliet's mother, a long, slow column of robed nuns files into the woods. Close-up of the nuns, each completely hidden beneath her robes. The sound of wind blowing.

JULIET
    Go away!

Dolores and her lover embrace. Behind, the nuns file slowly past. Wind.

CUT

Juliet's doctor walks over to her.

DOCTOR
    Dear Juliet, what were you saying?
JULIET
    Nothing. It's a game.
DOCTOR
    It would be better if you smoked less, Juliet. Listen to your doctor.

He walks away.

CUT

Juliet's face. Although her lips don't move, we hear her voice.

JULIET
    Can't you see them?

CUT

One of Juliet's nieces sits on the lawn by the beach ball. The procession of nuns passes behind her. Camera moves along the line of nuns to a nude woman standing in front of a huge, upright oyster shell.

JULIET
　　Take your revenge!

CUT

On the sawed-off top of a very tall, column-straight tree trunk sits the naked red-bearded man, his finger raised above his head in admonition.

JULIET
　　Forgive me, but who can I trust?

CUT

A naked woman, shiny with sweat or water, lies against the trunk of a tree wrapped in huge, black serpentine coils.

JULIET
　　. . . Life is all sacrifice.

CUT

Juliet standing on the lawn. The nuns file behind her.

JULIET
　　. . . Be more feminine; we'll teach you. My life is full of people who talk, talk, talk!

She turns and shouts aloud.

　　Get out! All of you! Go away!

CUT

Couples dance slowly, sexually on the lawn. No one responds to Juliet's shouts. The camera swings across the dancers to José, standing serenely in front of Juliet. He holds a glass in his hand, contemplating it.

JOSÉ

When I want something absolutely pure, trustworthy,
I always ask for water. We have a great need for simple
things, things which don't hide something else. Don't
be afraid of the truth—truth makes us free. After all,
what do you care about other people's reactions? In my
country we have a proverb that says: "I am my own
roof, my own window, my own hearth. My words are
my food, my thoughts are my drink. Thus am I happy."

CUT

José and Juliet dance together. José dances slowly, elegantly, with great sympathy and reserve.

JULIET

Are you real? . . . What should I do?

JOSÉ

I can't advise you. I want only that you live well.

JULIET

Where's Giorgio?

Juliet breaks away from José and looks around. Almost
everyone has left the party. A few guests drive away outside the gates. Elisabetta walks back into the yard through
the gate.

ELISABETTA

Your husband left earlier. He said he didn't want to
disturb you because you were dancing. He excuses himself, but he says he must meet some Brazilians, and
won't be able to come back for dinner. He said he'd
call you.

Camera pans across the empty lawn. The lawyer walks up
to Juliet.

LAWYER

Listen to me, my dear Juliet. To prove adultery, it's no
longer necessary to catch them *in flagrante;* circum-
stantial evidence is enough. I'm not talking to you as

your lawyer now, but as a friend who thinks highly of you, appreciates you, and likes you. Is there any hope for me? Listen to me; it is in your own interest. Good-bye.

JULIET

Good-bye.

Camera swings to Dr. Miller, who walks toward Juliet.

DR. MILLER

I'm bold enough to state that I understand your trouble: You identify too closely with your problem. . . .

CUT

Juliet and Dr. Miller walk through the pine woods.

DR. MILLER

. . . These ancient trees are the most impressive symbol of this way of life. They are deeply, securely rooted. Up there their branches spread open in all directions. Yet they grow spontaneously. This is a great, simple secret to learn—to fulfill yourself spontaneously, yet without putting yourself in conflict with your desires, your passions. Don't you feel how fine it is to be here? Sometimes it is necessary for us to speak—in a loud voice—even if it's a stranger who listens. Lie down here in the grass; relax. Don't be afraid. Look at the sun shining through the branches. Everything is peaceful, serene. Why?

Juliet sits tensely against a tree trunk. Dr. Miller lies on her stomach on the floor of the forest, like a young child completely at home in the woods.

JULIET

I don't know.

DR. MILLER

But what are you afraid of? May I answer? You're afraid of being alone, of being abandoned. You'ᴇᴇ afraid that your husband is going to leave you. And yet you want nothing more than to be left alone; you want your husband to go away.

Juliet laughs at this idea, ridiculing it, laughing at its incredible inappropriateness.

JULIET

I want Giorgio to leave me?

DR. MILLER

Exactly. Without Giorgio you'll start to breathe, to live, to become yourself. You think you're afraid. Actually you fear only one thing—to be happy.

CUT

Juliet enters a large, well-furnished apartment. A maid greets her.

JULIET

Miss Gabriella Olsen?

MAID

She's not in, but she shouldn't be late. . . I'm sorry—I was cleaning up. She called up at about noon to tell me that she wasn't coming back for lunch—these days she's often out. Excuse me, do you care for something?

JULIET

No, thank you.

Juliet sits stiffly on a sofa. The camera pans around the room. Wool and yarn lie in a knitting basket on a table. Masculine knicknacks are everywhere. The maid goes into an adjoining room, where she packs a suitcase as she continues to talk.

MAID

I'm sorry, but I have to finish packing. Are you a friend of Signora Gabriella? What does she say? Will she leave this time? Last time everything was all arranged, but at the last minute he calls her up and says, "Sorry, we can't leave!" No, he didn't do it maliciously—he's such a nice man. I never saw anybody so much in love with Signora Gabriella. And she really deserves it—though I shouldn't say so, because I'm a distant relative. But they're so sweet together. He says he feels right at home here. He chose the furniture, piece by piece. Have you noticed? Everything is in very good taste.

The telephone rings. The maid answers it.

Hello? . . . Good afternoon. . . . I'm packing for you. There is a lady waiting for you. . . . I don't know—I don't know her. Want to speak to her? . . .

To Juliet:

Signora, do you want to speak to Signora Gabriella?

JULIET

Yes, please.

MAID

Just a second. Take the call there—the phone is just behind you.

The telephone is on a table behind the sofa. Juliet gets up and walks around to it. As she picks up the phone, she sees a photograph of Giorgio's face standing on the table.

JULIET

Hello?

GABRIELLA

Who is this?

JULIET

I am Giorgio's wife.

GABRIELLA

Glad to meet you—but did we have an appointment?

JULIET

No, but I want to talk to you.

GABRIELLA

Can I help you? Can you tell me on the phone?

JULIET

I'll wait for you here. I'm not in a hurry.

GABRIELLA

I don't think you'd better. I mean, I have a very busy

afternoon, and I'm going to be late.

JULIET

What's the matter? Are you afraid?

GABRIELLA

Afraid? No. But I don't enjoy someone else's defeat. Besides, I don't think we have anything to talk about. Good night. Good luck.

JULIET

I'm staying here!

CUT

Night. The maid has turned out all the lights and is about to leave the apartment.

MAID

Signora, I have to leave. I think that Signora Gabriella will come back very late. . . . I'm sorry, but . . .

Juliet nods in acquiescence. She leaves the apartment.

CUT

Night. Juliet's house. Lights inside illuminate the downstairs windows. The small decorative trees along the path have been covered with transparent plastic. The camera moves along the path toward the front door.

CUT

Giorgio, seen through the doorway of the bedroom, packing.

CUT

Juliet enters the front door. Teresina works in the kitchen. The TV set is turned on, showing a commercial. Two lovers kiss blissfully, break, and say in unison:

. . . our happiness has only one name . . .

TERESINA
>Good evening, signora. I'm fixing dinner for your hus-
>band, because he's leaving.

Giorgio carries his suitcases into the room.

GIORGIO
>Teresina, take these suitcases out to the car. . . . You
>know, Juliet, that I have to go to Milan. I'll eat a little
>something and then I must leave.

JULIET
>I'll fix you something.

GIORGIO
>Never mind—Teresina is fixing it.

Juliet walks into the kitchen, looks at what is cooking on
the stove, and speaks to Teresina.

JULIET
>Did you add salt?

TERESINA
>No, signora.

Juliet adds salt to a pot on the stove.

JULIET
>What vegetables did you make?

TERESINA
>A few potatoes, Signora.

CUT

Giorgio stands nervously at the windows. On the TV, clowns
and dancers entertain. Teresina brings Giorgio's dinner to
the table.

TERESINA
>It's ready, sir. Is the trunk of the car unlocked?

GIORGIO
>Yes.

TERESINA
    Then I'll take them outside.

Teresina carries the bags out. Giorgio sits down and eats—
methodically, without appetite.

JULIET
    It's the first time you've ever packed by yourself.
GIORGIO
    Yes.
JULIET
    Are you sure you didn't forget anything?
GIORGIO
    No, I don't think so.
JULIET
    Will you be away long?
GIORGIO
    I told you—a couple of days. At any rate, I'll call you.

Juliet absently watches the TV set. On the TV screen an
entertainer turns to face the TV camera, and as he does,
we move in for a close-up. The entertainer smiles—a sad
clown's bittersweet smile.

CUT

Teresina returns from the car.

TERESINA
    I'll close the windows. After that may I go out for a
    while?
JULIET
    Yes, yes.
GIORGIO
    Listen, Juliet—I may be away longer than a couple of
    days. I'm not feeling too well. Today I went to the doc-
    tor. I didn't tell you, but . . .

The phone rings. Giorgio stops in midsentence. He says
nothing and does not answer the telephone, nor does Juliet.
The phone rings only once. There is a severe silence. Then

Juliet, still wearing her overcoat, walks to a sideboard and brings a bowl of fruit to Giorgio.

JULIET

Do you want some fruit?

GIORGIO

Thank you.

As she puts the bowl on the table, Giorgio reaches up to take her arm, but Juliet walks away.

GIORGIO

Lately I've overtired myself at work. The doctor said it is nothing serious, but that a short rest would do me good. . . . Frankly, I need to be alone for a while. . . .

Juliet goes to a closet and hangs up her coat, then walks to the windows and looks out across the lawn.

CUT

Afternoon. Juliet stands outside in front of the hedge at the edge of the lawn, dressed exactly as she was a moment ago. The camera pans across the lawn to Giorgio, Sylva, Adele, and Juliet's mother. All look exactly as they did the last time they appeared. Sylva runs across the lawn and takes Giorgio by the hand.

SYLVA

Ah, finally! I wanted to meet you so much! I heard so much about you. Oh! You're much better than I thought you'd be. Very good!

She leads Giorgio across the lawn to her mother and Adele.

. . . Mother, Juliet's fiancé.

MOTHER

How do you do?

CUT

Juliet stands at the window. Behind her Giorgio continues eating.

GIORGIO

Juliet, I think that people have told you distorted things, maliciously, with evil intentions. It is true that between that person and myself there has been a . . . friendship, a deep friendship. But nothing definite, nothing irreparable has happened. . . . The truth is that I'm going through a period of uncertainty, of confusion. . . . I want to be alone.

CUT

Juliet sits on the window seat.

CUT

Juliet and Giorgio asleep in bed. They lie close together, holding hands. Giorgio isn't wearing eyeshades.

CUT

Juliet sits on the window seat.

CUT

Giorgio sits on the other side of the room on a straight-backed chair. He wears his overcoat. Nervously, he pats his hands together. He gets up and walks over to Juliet.

GIORGIO

Good-bye, then, Juliet. I'll call you.

CUT

Giorgio and Gabriella embrace in a convertible sports car. A silent wind blows Gabriella's hair. Brown leaves swirl past them.

CUT

Juliet sits on the window seat.

JULIET
    Yes.

Giorgio bends and kisses her on both cheeks. He walks to
the door.

GIORGIO
    I'll call you as soon as I get there.
JULIET
    All right.
GIORGIO
    I don't know when—maybe tomorrow.
JULIET
    All right.
GIORGIO
    Oh—the mail: Put it aside.
JULIET
    Of course. The mail.
GIORGIO
    Good-bye, Juliet.
JULIET
    Yes.

Giorgio closes the door behind him.

CUT

The empty living room, the empty staircase, Giorgio's empty
place at the table.

CUT

Juliet sits on the window seat.

CUT

Night. A black canvas pavilion, strangely illuminated, billows
in heavy wind.

CUT

Lynx-eyes, dressed in a black Homburg and red bathrobe. The camera pans across a dark nighttime field to a landing barge illuminated by torches. Brush fires burn behind it. The wind blows. Three men carry the large, flapping canopy slowly over the field. Valli, dressed in his white suit, walks under it.

CUT

Juliet walks across the room and closes the shutters. She sits down to watch the TV. A couple dances gracefully. Suddenly Juliet begins to cry. She bends forward, sobbing, and we hear a girl's voice:

> Juliet, do you remember me?

CUT

Laura, dressed as in the children's play, lies at the bottom of a shallow pool of clear water. Her voice continues:

> . . . Do what I did. Here, everything is gray stillness and silence. . . .

CUT

The living-room sofa. The robes of a nun protrude slightly out beyond one corner.

> . . . Come with me—a long sleep, with no more pain. . . .

JULIET
    Laura!

CUT

Juliet sits before the TV.

CUT

Across the living room, Gabriella's maid examines the material of Juliet's window curtains.

CUT

A row of draped nuns stands behind the sofa.

CUT

José's legs as he demonstrates a pass, frozen in midair above the stairway landing. This is a stop frame, and his legs—feet off the floor, toes pointed down, are motionless, but his fingers, at the top of the screen, tap in boredom against his thigh.

CUT

Genius, in full costume, cape streaming out behind, leaping through the front doors into the house, frozen in midair, by another stop frame.

CUT

Juliet runs her fingers through her hair, near distraction.

CUT

Two German officers in Nazi S.S. uniforms and raincoats march past just outside the living-room windows. The wind blows.

CUT

Juliet on the TV couch, staring.

CUT

Susy's godson stands at the other end of the living room. A row of nuns stands behind him.

CUT

José sitting on a couch, bored, frozen in a stop frame. A row of nuns is lined up against the windows behind him.

CUT

JULIET
    It's not real! You don't exist! Go away!

CUT

The living room is empty.

CUT

The faces of Lola and Susy's two maids peek up over the back of the sofa, in front of them, two rows of nuns, one kneeling, one standing. In her basket, dressed in a bikini, Susy descends into the living room from the balcony above. Susy changes into another woman from her party.

CUT

Lynx-eyes, Valli, and Grillo sit on the sofas. Lynx-eyes spoons something out of a bowl, smacks his lips.

LYNX-EYES
    Very good! Very tasty! The very best!

CUT

JULIET
    You don't exist! Go away!

CUT

An ancient horse-drawn hearse, an old man on the coachman seat.

CUT

Arlette stands in the living room.

ARLETTE
It's Laura, your friend who killed herself for love. It's
Laura, your friend who killed herself for love. It's Laura,
your friend who killed herself for love.

As Arlette speaks, the hearse rolls past outside the windows.
The hearse bears a draped coffin. On top of it is a skull.
The camera follows the hearse and then catches a crowd of
Juliet's friends looking into the room through the windows—
Dolores, her lover, Elena, Valentina, etc.—and we hear the
voice of Juliet's doctor.

DOCTOR
Buy a horse, take long rides and swims. . . .

The doctor appears in the living room.

. . . buy a horse, buy a horse.

CUT

The living room. A horse close-up in the foreground; the
lawyer in the middle of the room; Genius, at the far end of
the room, juggles oranges. The lawyer steps forward and
kneels.

LAWYER
Is there any hope for me?

CUT

Dr. Miller lies on the floor on her stomach in front of a row
of nuns.

DR. MILLER
. . . without Giorgio you'll begin to breathe, to become
yourself, to become yourself. . . .

A man in a bathing suit climbs the stairs.

CUT

Under the stairway—a Nazi S.S. officer, women from Susy's party, Juliet's and Giorgio's friends.

CESARINO

> Your wife has spent the whole evening with me. Your wife has spent the whole evening with me. Your wife has spent the whole evening with me. . . .

CUT

Framed between two rows of hooded nuns, Roman soldiers, dressed in the same costumes of the children's play, march forward, and crash the butts of their spears on the floor.

CUT

Grandfather's airplane flies above Juliet's yard.

GRANDFATHER

> I can't come down, I can't land! It's your fault, Juliet— it all depends on you!

CUT

The red-bearded man stands two stories high, his head towering above the balcony over the living room.

LAURA'S VOICE

> A long sleep . . .

CUT

Susy in her basket, hanging above the living room. She smiles.

CUT

The living room is full of people—rows of nuns in the background; Lynx-eyes in a red bathrobe on the sofa; Susy in her basket; José standing bored; a horse on one side.

A nude woman leans against a wall in the foreground, her back turned. Beneath a filmy net scarf her buttocks are clearly defined.

CUT

Juliet in her bedroom. She walks to the bathroom.

CUT

The living room. Nuns file away at the right. Other nuns hover in front of the windows. The Nazi officers stare straight ahead in the left foreground. Lynx-eyes smiles, strikes a dancer's pose in the middle of the room. Little Juliet, Lola, and Susy's maids watch. Valli applauds. A wild African leaps into the air. A woman and a naked man rise toward the balcony in Susy's basket. The wind blows loudly.

CUT

Juliet walks from the bathroom to the bedroom. She gets into bed and tries to read. At the foot of the bed, her mother appears, exactly as Juliet recalled her to Valentina—the evil queen of children's stories, elegant but cold.

JULIET
    Mother! Help me! *You* help me!

Her mother does not answer.

JULIET
    I heard crying.
MOTHER
    It's the wind.
JULIET
    They're calling me!
MOTHER
    Don't move! Obey your mother!

CUT

A small door about three feet high has been cut in the bedroom wall. It is outlined by light shining behind it.

JULIET
    I have to go!
MOTHER
    Don't move!

Juliet gets out of bed and goes to the little door. It has no handle. She kneels in front of it and claws at its edges.

JULIET
    Who are you? Who are you? Open!
MOTHER
    Don't open it! Obey me!

Juliet faces her mother.

    You don't frighten me any more.

Without being touched, the little door snaps open. Juliet pulls it wide. Behind it there is a long hall with white walls and a rough plank floor. Midway down the corridor little Juliet lies on her grill, her hands tied in the position of prayer.

CUT

The people in the living room, exactly as before, but frightened.

CUT

Juliet crawls through the door to little Juliet and begins to untie her hands.

CUT

The adult Juliet, in bed. She writhes as if struggling to free herself.

CUT

The people in the living room in postures of fear. They fade and, without moving their limbs, are drawn backward out of the house, like a tableau of phantoms returning to another dimension.

CUT

Inside the tiny hall Juliet frees little Juliet and embraces her. Little Juliet walks away down the hall.

CUT

Juliet's mother, suddenly aged and bent, turns as if to leave.

CUT

Grandfather stands beside his airplane on the front lawn. Little Juliet runs to him.

GRANDFATHER
> Look who's here. My little Beefsteak! How are you? Where'd you leave your grill?

He takes her hand and they walk across the lawn.

> Let's say good-bye to those boors.

CUT

All the characters of the hallucinations ride on a huge, cumbersome wagon loaded with their appurtenances. The grill and Susy's basket hang ignominiously from a pole at the rear. The prow of the landing barge sways off one side. Part of the cart is covered by tattered remains of the huge canopy that covered Valli on the burning field. Laura's hearse rolls dismally alongside the wallowing, swaying cart.

CUT

Grandfather and little Juliet wave good-bye to the cart.

CUT

Juliet stands at the door of her house, smiling.

CUT

The cart recedes.

CUT

Grandfather begins to climb back into his plane. He points to Fanny, posed on the wing, smiling hugely.

GRANDFATHER

Here's my lovely Fatso! And now we have to go.

CUT

Juliet, at the front door.

JULIET

Take me with you, Grandpa.

GRANDFATHER

But where? This is an old plane; it doesn't go anywhere. It only had to come this far.

CUT

Laughing, Fanny smacks a great good-bye kiss to Juliet. Grandfather starts the plane.

GRANDFATHER

Good-bye. Don't hold on to me—you don't need me any longer. I, too, am an invention of yours; but you are full of life.

CUT

Little Juliet walks across the lawn, waving good-bye. She dissolves into the air.

GRANDFATHER

Good-bye, Little Beefsteak.

CUT

The lawn is empty. Juliet walks out through the gate and stands on the edge of a broad, open field. Borne on the air comes the sound of urgent voices, thin and high. They whisper:

Juliet. . . . Juliet. . . . Juliet. . . .

JULIET

Who are you?

VOICES

True friends, true friends, true friends. Now, if you want us to, we can stay, we can stay, we can stay. . . . Listen to us, listen closely. . . .

Juliet walks toward the pine woods. The trees glow green and lovely in brilliant, warm sunlight.

END

COMING SOON FROM COLUMBIA PICTURES . . .
ON SALE NOW IN BALLANTINE BOOKS!

THE INTERROGATORS

A GRIM HOUR-BY-HOUR NOVEL OF THE SEARCH TO FIND A SEX KILLER • SOON TO BE A MAJOR MOTION PICTURE!

"STARKLY RUTHLESS!"
—Chicago Daily News

ALLAN PRIOR

To order by mail, send 75¢ plus 5¢ for postage and handling to: Dept. CS, Ballantine Books, 101 Fifth Avenue, New York, N. Y. 10003 (Be sure to include your Zip Code number in your address!)

Nikos Kazantzakis'
FIERY NOVEL OF A MODERN PAGAN
"ALIVE WITH ENERGY... EARTHY AND RABELAISIAN"

Saturday Review

NOW A 20th CENTURY-FOX FILM

ZORBA
THE GREEK

A magnificently vital novel of the pleasures of the flesh, the wonder and mystery of the universe. Steeped in the sensual joy, the anguish, brutality and glory of life, Zorba is one of the great creations of modern fiction.

U6020   352 pages   75¢

To order by mail, send price of book plus 5¢ postage and handling to: Dept. CS, Ballantine Books, 101 Fifth Avenue, New York, N. Y. 10003.

Gramley Library
Salem College
Winston-Salem, NC 27108